# THE
# DOCTORS
## GUIDE TO

*Starting Your Practice Right*

# DR. CORY S. FAWCETT

*The Doctors Guide to Starting Your Practice Right*
By Dr. Cory S. Fawcett © 2016

Print ISBN: 978-1-61206-116-0
eBook ISBN: 978-1-61206-117-7

Interior and Cover Design: Fusion Creative Works, fusioncw.com
Lead Editor: Jennifer Regner

For more information, visit DrCorySFawcett.com

Published by

AlohaPublishing.com
First Printing
Printed in the United States of America

# Dedication

Name _____

Address _____

 Date _____

I dedicate this book to the hardworking medical students and residents, their families, and the schools that support them. My hope is you will start your practice right and build the wonderful life you deserve.

Signature _____ **Dr. Cory S. Fawcett**

# Contents

# Introduction

When I completed my residency and ventured into the world of private practice, I had no one to guide me. No classes were available on how to find the job that was right for me or how to adapt to my new life as an attending physician. I was working nearly 100 hours a week and didn't have much time to think about the transition. My mentors taught me about medicine and surgery, and they were great, but no one taught me about business or life.

There were many questions on my mind: What to look for in a colleague or partner? What makes a good practice? Do I want to be employed, or would I rather own a practice? How do I know if an employment or partnership contract is fair and includes the important points? Is it possible to have a home life better than the one I experienced in residency?

I muddled through the transition with a few hiccups along the way, but overall, I can't complain. My new partners taught me how to run a practice and led me to some great advisors: an accountant, an attorney, and a pastor.

I was lucky. I could have just as easily ended up with partners and advisors who were struggling, misinformed, or worse.

Over the years, I began noticing doctors who were not doing as well, financially, as they could be. For me, the straw that broke the camel's back was the day a physician told me she was making $450,000 a year and still needed to moonlight to make ends meet. That should not be happening, and it broke my heart. With a salary like that, she should be living a great life. She had no one to show her a better way.

Life is easier when an experienced guide pulls up beside you and shows you better options. There is no reason for any doctor to begin a career flying blind and potentially heading the wrong direction. It can be difficult to recover from mistakes made at this key juncture in your life and career, such as buying the house of your dreams rather than the house of your income, or choosing a practice for the wrong reasons. It's a time when you don't know what you don't know.

Yes, there is life after residency. A busy practicing professional *can* have a great home life and career without working as hard as a resident. You *can* run a practice and still watch your kids grow up; you don't have to miss their once-in-a-lifetime milestones because you were too busy working. Burnout need not be in the equation. Debt doesn't have to rule your life. You can take control of your future and live the dream you chased when you were just a kid who wanted to be a doctor. Remember that dream?

This book will help you set goals, define and find your dream job, negotiate your contract, pay off your student loans, invest for your retirement, manage your workload, find time for weekends off and vacations, and so much more. You will meet Dr. Rolex and Dr. Timex, who have differing attitudes about spending money, and see how their approaches affect their future wealth.

Let me be your guide through this important transition in your life, where taking the right first steps could make all the difference.

# Chapter 1

# THE RIGHT START MAKES ALL THE DIFFERENCE

## HEADING IN THE RIGHT DIRECTION

You've almost made it. You're entering the home stretch and thinking about that first job. Everything you've done—four years of college, four years of medical school, then three to eight years of residency—has been leading to this. It's finally time to think about your own practice.

It's a bit scary to take that first step. No more leaning on the attending. You've morphed into the attending like a butterfly emerging from its cocoon, and now all the responsibility lies with you.

The decisions you make during the next few years will impact the rest of your life, either positively or negatively. The location of your first job, the type of practice you join, the cost of your house, and the other crossroads you negotiate will all play a role in formulating your future. Making a mistake here can create a big effect later. This book will help you choose what's right for you and avoid the critical errors.

If you were to take off on a flight across the country, say from San Francisco to Washington, D.C., a small and seemingly insignificant miscalculation of direction could make you miss your destination.

Starting just five degrees off course is not too noticeable in the first 100 yards, when you are only 26 feet off course. That's less than the length of the wing, no big deal. By the time you get to the other side of the country, you will miss your destination by more than 200 miles. Ouch. If on the other hand, you were in a rocket headed to the moon, you would miss the moon by almost 21,000 miles, or almost ten times the diameter of the moon, by starting just five degrees off trajectory. Can you say *lost in space?*

Buying a house sooner, or bigger, or more expensive than you need, for example, could take you a long way from where you want to be in the future. Some advisors believe your house is a good investment, and sometimes it's true, but mostly your house is your biggest expense. There's a reason the mortgage doesn't show up in the investment section of a budgeting plan. If your housing expense is too high, you could find yourself in a financial bind for many years, with significant impacts in multiple areas of your life and finances.

## THE RIGHT START MAKES ALL THE DIFFERENCE

If you follow your real estate agent's advice and buy the most expensive house your paycheck allows, you will be left with too little money for other things you need. A ripple effect will occur. You won't be able to pay off your school loans quickly, or have enough money left to invest for retirement or to set aside for your children's college education. You may not be able to travel to your desired vacation destinations. Maybe you're forced to take on extra work to cover the bills. That one decision will haunt you for years to come.

If, on the other hand, you were to buy a nice house that fits comfortably into your budget, this slightly different trajectory creates a different ripple effect. Now you have money to pay off your student loans. You can max out your retirement plan contributions. Your children will be able to graduate from college debt-free. The trip to Paris is still on the horizon. With fewer bills, you can cut back your hours a little and come home for dinner every night. One simple decision—the cost of your house—can have a positive or a negative effect on the rest of your life, magnified and spread out over the whole family. This minor trajectory difference early on turns into a huge financial impact by the time 40 years has passed.

Multiply this effect by all the other decisions you will be making during this transition and you can either find yourself headed for trouble, or headed for a wonderful and fulfilling career and home life.

Consider the ripple effect of right or wrong decisions in the following areas:

✓ The town you live in

✓ Your professional partners

✓ The distance from your extended family

✓ Proximity to the type of recreation you enjoy, like skiing, surfing, or fishing

✓ Availability of your religious denomination

If you do make some bad decisions and have to change direction, some of the corrections can be very expensive and take a high emotional toll.

What happens if you don't like your partners or the city you live in, and have to find another job? You may have a problem getting out of the contract. Some advances may need to be paid back. You may have to pay for a very expensive "tail" (coverage for when you leave a practice) on your malpractice insurance. You incur another set of moving costs. Your house may not sell. You have to find new friends. Your children will need to start at a new school. All these issues not only take a bite out of your finances, but also your time, your energy, and your family's well-being.

Here's a little background on how I found my first job. My wife and I both grew up in Oregon. Most of my family lives in southern Oregon, around Medford. Most of her family lives in northern Oregon, near Portland. We knew living close enough to visit our families was going to be an important part of our lives for many years to come. We set out to find a practice between the two locations.

I began my search and contacted a physician recruiter. I told the recruiter we were only willing to take a position on Interstate 5 between Medford and Portland. This would situate us between our two extended families for the rest of our lives.

Initially the recruiter didn't find anything there, so he started presenting other locations. His pay depended on finding me a job. He called one day to ask if I was interested in a really good job in Idaho. I asked him if Idaho was between Medford and Portland on Interstate 5. He wasn't amused. The job he was proposing was 450 miles away from where I wanted to live. He said there was nothing available where I wanted to live, so I should expand my options. I told him no.

The part of the country where we wanted to spend the rest of our lives was not negotiable. I was not willing to take a good-paying job if it didn't fit my needs. Such compromise would guarantee my dissatisfaction and I would end up looking for another job later. He was very unhappy with my narrow thinking and told me I would never find what I sought.

Since nothing was advertised where I wanted to live, I decided to go hunting for what was not advertised. I called every hospital between Medford and Portland on Interstate 5, looking for openings. Six practices were thinking about adding another surgeon, but had not yet advertised the position. I made a road trip to Oregon and interviewed at all six practices, and landed my dream job.

Starting a journey pointing in the wrong direction will never get you to the destination you seek. A lifetime of happiness hinges on the decisions you make as you head into your first practice. I stuck to my guns and found my dream job in Grants Pass, Oregon—on Interstate 5 between Medford and Portland.

This decision set off some ripples. I was able to spend holidays with my extended family. There was never a year when I didn't have the time or money to fly home for Thanksgiving. If I was on call, we celebrated Thanksgiving at my house and since everyone lived nearby, it wasn't a problem. If I got called to the hospital, only I missed out, and no one else.

My children got to know their grandparents, aunts, uncles, and cousins. Relatives were able to attend my children's school functions and sporting events. The weather was to my liking. I could stay in touch with some of my high school friends and didn't need to travel to reunions. A small fortune on travel expenses was avoided. I helped my parents and grandparents as they aged. Grandparents were available as sitters when needed. My family and I enjoyed a long list of benefits and rewards

because I thought about what I wanted, and took m
where I wanted to live.

Decide in what direction your happiness lies and head for it. Do not pass go, do not collect $200, and for heaven's sake don't get off course, not even five degrees.

> ### The journey of a thousand leagues begins with a single step.
>
> ### – Lao Tzu

Make sure your journey begins in the right direction.

## UNDERSTANDING WHAT YOU WANT

What is your dream job? It's the one you would do every day, even if no one paid you. When you find it, you never really go to work each day, you go and play. If you truly enjoy and look forward to each workday, burnout is less likely. Are there any jobs like that out there for doctors? Yes, there are. But before you can go out and find it, you must first define what it looks like.

The first step in defining a dream job is to ask yourself what you really want—and figure out who you are. A teacher, inventor, leader, follower, loaner, team player, employee, or employer? What makes you tick? Understanding your deep-rooted nality characteristics is important. If you need help with

ask some friends, relatives, or your spouse. Maybe even

a personality test. When you fully understand what drives

and what kind of person you are, then you can set out to

nd a practice to fit.

If research is not your thing, then looking for a university position will be a bad idea. Happiness will elude you in that setting. If you know you are a small-town kind of person, then looking at the jobs in New York City, even though the pay is higher, will be a recipe for disaster.

One of the biggest factors in your future well-being is job satisfaction. Spend as much time as you need to define exactly what it is you are looking for, and then you will know it when you see it.

## REALIZING MONEY ISN'T THE FIRST PRIORITY

Don't let money be the deciding factor; it's never the most important thing. One of the first criteria a young doctor with lots of debt looks for in a job is the salary. I know it seems counterintuitive, but salary is at the bottom of the list of important factors in picking a job. Remember, you want to find a job you would do for free anyway. If they have to pay you to do it, it's work. If you are doing it because you love it and just happen to get paid, that's a great career.

You will make plenty of money at almost all of the opportunities, so don't let money be your guide. Making a choice based solely on salary is almost always a setup for disappointment.

Many young doctors are driven to choose a position in an underserved area for either a loan forgiveness benefit or an outrageously high starting salary (salary may be unusually high if the job has undesirable aspects and/or has been vacant for a long time). Their debt is so overwhelming that it takes the driver's seat in the decision making.

No amount of loan forgiveness will be enough to keep you happy if you don't like the job or the location. Salary has a way of losing its luster when you dread going to the office. Make your choice based first on the work you'll be doing; if you love the position and work hard, the income will be sufficient.

I met one doctor who was looking at two positions in the same town, one as a hospital employee and the other in a private practice partnership. I asked him what his thoughts were about the two opportunities. He told me he was going to take the employed position at the hospital because it would be easier to leave than a partnership. I couldn't believe my ears. He was deciding to take his first job as a physician at the same time as he was planning to leave that same job. He had not bothered to take the time to figure out what he wanted to do or where he wanted to live, so he was going to take something that would be easy to quit when he figured it out.

He didn't consider the expense, pain, and anguish that go into leaving one practice to start another. Why, after all those years of training, would he ever settle for less than the best for himself and his family?

He did move somewhere else less than two years later, before his contract was up. Since the hospital had given him an advance and he left early, he had to repay part of his advance. How much better would it have been to take the position he wanted in the first place? Life is too short for that kind of nonsense. The impacts of that decision can be far reaching, including another house move, another hospital system to learn, a new town, a new school for the kids, another job search for his spouse, leaving friends behind, and on and on.

# CHANGING PRACTICES COSTS MONEY

A friend of mine shared the costs of his job change with me. The details show an example of the financial impact changing jobs can have for a physician:

- ✓ $10,000 in lost income during time off for interview trips
- ✓ $40,000 malpractice insurance tail
- ✓ $5,000 net cost to move across the country ($15,000 total minus $10,000 paid by new employer)
- ✓ $1,000 for new state licensing and hospital privileges
- ✓ $60,000 in lost income during the three months it took to obtain new licensing and privileges
- ✓ $24,000 in house payments during the ten months it took to sell the first house
- ✓ $3,000 in extra property taxes on the first house
- ✓ $800 in extra homeowners insurance on the first house
- ✓ $20,000 real estate agent's fee to sell the first house
- ✓ $1,000 in closing costs on the sale of the first house
- ✓ $10,000 in closing costs for the new house

The total cost for the job change was $174,800.

Every job change will negatively impact your net worth. I know doctors who have changed jobs several times during their career.

When I decided to take the position in Grants Pass, it fit everything I wanted for my job and my family's life. Consequently, I worked for over twenty years in that practice and became part of the community, and it became part of me. It became my home.

I've seen lots of doctors who didn't—or couldn't—figure out what they wanted, and moved from practice to practice every few years as a result. When you ask their kids where they are from, they are not sure how to answer.

Your family's happiness will depend heavily on your happiness. So find out what your dream is and go get it. Don't settle for anything less than the spectacular life you were meant to live. Otherwise, all those years of training were for naught.

## INTRODUCING DR. ROLEX AND DR. TIMEX

You will begin your career with preconceptions about how to best utilize money. You learned these from your parents, your friends, and the media. Beliefs on borrowing, saving, and spending will shape your decisions and consequently your future.

I'd like to introduce two characters whose choices will demonstrate the impact of two different ways to handle money. I've called them Dr. Rolex and Dr. Timex. These two doctors have similar incomes but different ideas about how to use money. They represent opposing philosophies which are neither good nor bad, but merely different. Taken to extremes, either philosophy has the potential to ruin your life in both the financial and relationship realms.

The two doctors have been in practice for several years now, so we can look back and see what effects their earlier decisions have created. Let's meet them now as we begin to follow their lives.

**DR. ROLEX** likes the finer things in life. Her watch is not only for telling time but also serves as a piece of jewelry and a statement about her financial status. To her, it says she has money; she is strong, she is bold, she is confident, and knows where she's going. It's a statement to the world that she has enough confidence in her earning potential to spend $10,000 on a watch.

She likes driving new cars. They smell good and are reliable. She replaces them every two years so they are always under warranty. Leases are her preferred method of acquiring them and she leans towards European luxury cars.

She and her husband prefer eating out at fine restaurants over cooking at home, so they don't waste a lot of time grocery shopping and slaving over a hot stove. For vacations, she likes the tropical beach scene the best and usually picks them from one of the two travel magazines she reads. She likes resorts with a kid's program so they have something fun to do while she and her husband enjoy reading and relaxing on the beach.

Her house is located on the country club's eighth fairway and the gardener keeps the yard looking immaculate. She subscribes to a pool cleaning service so her time is not spent on the mundane things like yard and pool care, but is available for her patients and family instead.

Dr. Rolex grew up with the belief that value is always found in higher quality items, so she only buys the best designer-label clothes. With her high income and many years ahead in her career, she is not worried by far-off things like retirement or her children's college costs. She will have plenty of time to take care of those things later. She feels it is more important to live in the present. The past is gone, and the future is a long way off. She feels working on a budget would not be time well spent. She has worked hard to get to this financial point in her life and feels like now is the time to enjoy it.

**DR. TIMEX** is a very practical person who seeks value for her money. She buys a good watch that looks nice and will dependably tell time—and hopefully was on sale. Her watch says she is dependable and fashionable, values her money, buys affordable quality, and knows where she's going.

She paid cash for her Ford Explorer and enjoys its versatility and practicality. She's hoping to get another five years out of it. Her husband enjoys cooking and she works hard to be home for dinner every night. She enjoys listening to her kids talk about the fun they had helping Dad make dinner. Her family enjoys weekends camping or playing at the beach. They go on family-friendly vacations, and this year will be traveling to Orlando, Florida.

Her house is located near the best school in town, allowing her children to walk to school every morning. It's a nice house in a good neighborhood. She enjoys working in the yard; it's a therapeutic change from the office, and the kids often join her so they can be doing something together.

Dr. Timex buys her clothing at a local department store. She and her family always look sharp and fashionable in the latest styles. Her husband and she would like to retire early and travel across Europe someday. She doesn't like to be in debt, and works to pay cash for everything she buys. Being prepared for unexpected things is important to her, and she keeps a budget to make sure everything will be covered. She works hard for her money and would like to keep as much of it as possible.

As you can see, Dr. Rolex and Dr. Timex live very different lives on similar incomes. You probably know someone just like each of these doctors. Financially, they are on different trajectories and we will see some big differences in their total wealth 30 years from now. They are both enjoying their lives at the moment and have no particular concerns for the future.

# Chapter 2

# DEFINING YOUR DREAM JOB

You can't find your dream job until you know what it looks like. The next few sections describe crucial aspects that will help you define it.

## EMPLOYMENT VERSUS OWNERSHIP MODELS

Recent trends in the practice of medicine have been shifting from a predominantly private practice model toward an employment model. Many factors are driving this. The popular emphasis on work-life balance has promoted the impression that it's better as an employee, which may not necessarily be true. Skyrocketing debt from training is making doctors reluctant to lay out money to buy into a practice. Healthcare reform has created uncertainty about how the industry will be affected, making a salaried position look more attractive.

I have practiced in both models, and experienced the good and the bad each has to offer. My first two years were as an employee of my future partnership. The next eighteen years were as a partner in a single specialty private practice. When I retired from that practice, I began working part-time, first as a private corporation (PC) doing locums, and then as an employee in a large hospital system. Since you will be practicing for 20 to 50 years, it is best to decide early which model seems best for you—but as you see from my history, the decision is not set in stone.

Every doctor is in a different situation at the beginning of their career. Some are single, some are single parents, some are married, and some are married with children. Some are entrepreneurs and some just want to see patients. Some are drowning in debt and some are only mildly in debt.

Whatever your current situation and whatever your future goals are, you should weigh the pros and cons of this choice and write them down. After looking over your list and realizing some items are more important than others, you should be able to make the decision best fitting your circumstances and your personality.

Take a look at the advantages and disadvantages of the two models and take note of those most important to you.

# ADVANTAGES OF OWNING YOUR PRACTICE

## Control

The number one most important reason for being the owner is control. When you own the business, you are the one in control. You shape your destiny and make the crucial decisions. If your nurse is not performing, get a new one. If your nurse is doing a great job, provide a reward. Don't like your electronic medical records program? Get a new one. Want Mondays off? Then take Mondays off. For many, control is an important factor.

## Profit potential

Another very important advantage is the upside of profit potential. The practice of medicine is a business. If you don't make a profit, the doors will close. If you make a great profit by providing a great service, you get to keep the profit. The more you work, the more you make.

I experienced this directly when I was beginning my practice. I knew an internist who did colonoscopies and was a hospital employee. If he was having a busy day and someone called for an urgent colonoscopy in the hospital, he would pass it on to me. His pay didn't increase if he added the case into his schedule, but mine did. I always took the case. A short time later, the hospital realized they were not making any profit off these primary care doctors and dumped them all. Suddenly, these doctors were in private practice and getting paid based on the services they provided.

This doctor never called me again to do a colonoscopy when he was busy. When he got paid extra to work it in, he found a way.

Some may see the profit potential of a private practice negatively, and view it as enslaving you to your practice. Recognize that in private practice you can accept the case or turn it away, if you don't have the time—but if you take it, you will be rewarded with extra income. As an employee, you will not likely be rewarded for the extra work.

As the owner, you can also create profit by providing ancillary services. You can offer imaging services in your office, like ultrasounds and x-rays. Additional businesses can come under your wing like the ENT (ear, nose, and throat) surgeon with an audiologist service, or the pulmonologist who also provides a sleep center, or a vascular surgeon with a vascular studies lab, or an orthopedic surgeon offering physical therapy. Most specialties have some sort of ancillary service to offer.

## Equity

When you own a practice, you will have something of value when you leave. You will have some accounts receivable yet to be collected. You may own part of a building—and since you have something to sell or rent, it will be a boost to your retirement income. I know one dentist who sold his practice, but the new dentist didn't want to assume more debt to buy the building. The retiring dentist was able to rent the building to the new dentist for a substantial boost in income during his retirement.

## Tax advantages

Business owners have greater tax advantages. Several tax write-offs are available to business owners that are not available to employees. The costs of traveling to conferences, purchasing a camera, covering your healthcare expenses, and having a home office are some of the deductions offered to business owners. The tax laws are tilted in the favor of owners. The bottom line: on the same salary, a business owner will have more spendable money than an employee.

## Retirement plans

You can put more money into your retirement plan when you own a business. As a business owner, you have several options for how to structure your retirement plans, and you can choose the one to best suit your needs.

## Vacation

You choose your vacation and time-off terms with almost unlimited flexibility. You are only limited by income. If you take more time off, your production will be lower but your well-being will be improved.

## Patient choice

If there are certain cases in your specialty you do not want to see, then don't. There is no reason to do the things you don't like. As the owner, you can choose what you want to do with your practice.

### Shared responsibility

The more partners you have, the less you will be responsible for when it comes to running the business. Your portion of the overhead is lower. Your share of the workload is lower.

### Immediate referral base

In a partnership, your partners already have a referral base for you to plug into. They want you to succeed and be busy, so they will begin to feed you cases right out of the gate.

## ADVANTAGES OF BEING AN EMPLOYEE

### Fewer hassles

There are none of the hassles of running a business. That responsibility is someone else's. Your boss will do the hiring and firing and make all the business decisions. You can focus on the practice of medicine.

### Practice viability

As an employee, you have a guaranteed income with no concern about your patients' ability to pay or their insurance status. You also have no worry about having enough patients. You will not need to advertise to boost your patient volume. You don't need to concern yourself with billing and collections. You only need to cash your paycheck. If the area is financially depressed, you may make more money being employed, as the hospital may subsidize your salary to keep their doors open.

## No overhead

As an employee, you have no additional costs. You won't be buying into a practice, which may be a significant benefit if you have lots of debt and no money in the bank. You won't need to buy your share of the building, or purchase any equipment. There are no overhead worries. You even get paid vacations.

## Higher initial salary

Employees usually get paid a higher income at first and it usually doesn't grow much from there. This is one of the things new doctors notice right away. Starting salaries as an employee tend to be higher. In fact, if the organization is in great need, the starting salary could be outrageously high.

## Flexibility

Leaving an employed position is often easier. You won't have a buyout agreement. You can give your notice and leave. Sometimes there may be something you need to pay back, if you leave too early. But if you are struggling with the decision, the option of an easy exit may be a real benefit.

## Automatic referrals

As an employed physician, you often walk into a situation where good patient volumes are a certainty. This is particularly true for a referral-based practice where the primary care physicians are also employees and are obligated by contract to send their patients to see you.

## DISADVANTAGES OF OWNING YOUR OWN PRACTICE

### Overhead expense

Startup costs are higher for those who own their practice. Owning something means buying something. If your debt burden is high, this may be unpalatable. Since you are responsible for the cost of improvements, every time the government throws a new regulation at your business, you are responsible for funding the new requirement. When HIPAA was forced on us, our office had to shoulder the cost of some required changes. As electronic medical records were made a requirement, we had to shoulder the cost. Since government mandates are a moving target, continual updates will be in your future.

When you bring on a new partner, it will cost you money initially. You, as the owner, will be paying the new partner's salary out of your pocket, and the new partner always starts with no patients and no accounts receivable. It takes a while before they are pulling their own load financially.

Practice overhead may prevent the possibility of working part-time. The office doesn't suddenly become half as expensive to run when you cut your working hours in half. The phone company doesn't cut their bill in half. The property taxes on your office don't go down. Your office staff isn't interested in taking a 50% pay cut. It could be financially impossible to work part-time.

## Vacation versus income

Taking vacations may be a difficult choice since overhead continues when you are gone. I often joked about my income going negative when I went on vacation. If this is worrisome to you, it may influence your decision to take the time off you need. You may be so worried about your overhead that you avoid the vacation completely and move closer to burnout.

One doctor I know would send his family on vacation while he stayed home and worked to keep the income stream positive. To combat this, you need to be thinking of your income on an annual basis and not on a daily basis. You will make enough, even with the vacation.

## Building a practice

As a physician entering a private practice, you need to build a referral base if you are a specialist. With time, your desire and ability to provide excellent care for your patients will likely make you as busy as you want to be, but this will not occur immediately.

### Management stress

Hiring and firing employees can be stressful as an owner, and this may fall on your shoulders. You can abdicate some of this by having an office manager and making it their job to take care of the staffing issues.

You will be making a lot more decisions as an owner: what 401(k) plan to use, which EMR to buy, do we need to expand the office, and is it time for a new partner are some examples. If decision making is not your strong point, this could be an issue for you. Researching and making the decisions will also take additional time.

## DISADVANTAGES OF BEING AN EMPLOYEE

### Little control

The biggest downside is having almost no control over what happens in the practice. You don't pick the office staff, the retirement plan, your hours, your vacation time, or anything else about the practice. You answer to an administrator. One hospital I know of hired a new doctor, and three months later still hadn't put her name on the office door. Granted, it is a small item, but if that's an example of where you stand in the priorities of the employer, you can be sure they will not be jumping in to help you when you need something important.

You will not be in control of picking your new partners. The employer will be deciding when it is time to bring on a new partner. If you are feeling overworked and ready to get another partner, it will happen only if your employer agrees. When it's time to get a new partner, they will likely invite you to the interview and listen to your input, but they will pick the partner. If you are getting paid based on a production formula, when they bring on a new partner, it may cut into your production and drop your pay.

You will have much less to say about when you take time off and how much you can take. The employer wants you working; when you are on vacation, you are not making them any money. They might not allow you to take a three week vacation, or even a couple hours off to attend your child's school performance.

Your retirement plan will be whatever they tell you it will be. Hopefully, they have a good one. It will likely have a maximum contribution that is lower than that of your colleagues in business for themselves. You will have less control as to how your money is invested as well.

Your employer will be deciding what equipment you use. You can make suggestions, but if you have a favorite tool you used in your training and they own a different one, you are unlikely to get them to fork out the money to buy the tool you want. They will tell you to use what they have.

## Fewer tax advantages

As an employee, there are few tax deductions available for you. The tax laws are not written in favor of the employee, they are written in favor of the employer.

## Less job security

Your employment is at their mercy. If they feel you aren't doing what they want, you will be terminated. One physician I know had a complication which prompted a look into all his cases. When the examination was complete, there were more complications than desired. He was called into a meeting and fired. No warning. No chance to see the results. No chance for improvement. You work as long as they want you to work and no more. If it becomes unprofitable for them to own you, the relationship will end abruptly.

## No equity

When you do leave, there is nothing to sell. You have equity in nothing. You don't own a building, or the accounts receivable, or any equipment. If you were the physician in the last paragraph, you got your last paycheck and were gone. No residual income for retirement, beyond that saved in your retirement plan.

## Production quotas

You may be required to meet a production quota. They hired you to make money for them and for no other reason. If you can't keep up with expected production, you could be fired.

Both groups of doctors, owners and employees, can be happy with their choice. If you think about it ahead of time and weigh the pros and cons for your personality, I think you will be able to pick the model that best suits you and you will also be happy with your choice. The contract negotiation section, later in the book, covers aspects applicable to both models and may help you to avoid, or at least mitigate, some of the disadvantages of either model.

## ACADEMIC VERSUS CLINICAL SETTING

This is another major branch point in your decision making. The life of a community doctor is very different from the life of one at a tertiary referral center, where you will handle the most complex cases, do research, and train the next generation of clinicians. Look at the following aspects of the practice of medicine, and determine whether the academic or clinical environment matches your preferences.

### Research and publications

Do you like doing medical research? Would you like to have 40 published papers before you are 40 years old? Do you want to write chapters in medical text books? If so, then you need to be thinking about finding a spot in a major teaching institution. You are unlikely to achieve these things in a private clinical practice.

Academic doctors tend to give more lectures, travel to present papers, sit on national committees, work with cutting-edge technology, give board exams, and are generally thought of as leaders in their specialty. They may help set standards. They tend to be experts who are constantly referred the toughest cases and tend to be in the big city.

## Teaching

Teaching medical students and residents is fun but not enjoyed by everyone. In an academic setting, you will be training future doctors. If you are a surgeon, a resident may be doing the operating while you talk them through the procedure. They are then responsible for doing the charting, which you review. In the clinical setting, you do the operating and the charting.

As a new attending, your need to produce good initial results may conflict with your desire to teach. You may fear the results of the resident will be inferior to doing it yourself. You also might not feel comfortable teaching someone skills you are still ironing out.

In a clinical environment, you are unlikely to have medical students or residents. Most of the teaching will be back and forth between you and your new partners, or the other physicians in town, which can be valuable to the new attending.

## Specialization potential

Each specialty has many different diagnoses they may treat. The bigger the institution, the smaller your area of expertise. A vascular surgeon at a university might only do vascular surgery and may be even more subspecialized. In a community setting, the vascular surgeon also takes general surgery call, and the practice might only be 50% vascular surgery. If you like working in a broader diagnostic area, then head towards a clinical job and away from a teaching institution. If a narrow focus of practice is your thing, bigger institutions will be your target.

## Clinical bread and butter

Clinical doctors, on the other hand, tend to be in smaller centers and do a broader range of care. If they run into something very complex, they have the option of shipping it away to a higher level of care or greater specialization. They spend more time doing bread and butter cases. They are unlikely to become famous in their field. Rather than be the department chair for many years, they tend to rotate through the job on a short cycle with the other clinicians. They can live in any size city they choose.

## Relationships with patients

Since many patients at a tertiary center are referred from far away, developing a long-term relationship with the patient and their family is not the norm. A university doctor is more likely to address the patient's complex problem, and then return them to their primary doctor's care. Clinical doctors can develop long-term relationships with their patients. They become a part of the community in which they live, on a different level than an academic doctor does.

# SMALL TOWNS VERSUS BIG CITIES

This is something you need to understand about yourself and your spouse. Are you a country mouse or a city mouse, as the old children's story goes? Both offer great perks but they are not the same perks. I remember one of my fellow residents stating he couldn't wait to get out of this small town and get back to Los Angeles. There was nothing to do in the small town. So I asked him what he wanted to do that we don't have. He said we only have a few movie theaters, but LA has hundreds. So I asked how many movies he went to last month, and he said none. I told him he could watch no movies here just as easily as in LA. It wasn't actually going to the movies that excited him; it was having more available options. He was definitely a city mouse and there was no convincing him otherwise.

### Big city

The cost of living in a big city tends to be higher than in a smaller town. The higher population density will make the traffic conditions worse. You are likely to live farther from work and the commute will impact your schedule, taking time away from your family on a daily basis. Your housing choices will be smaller and more expensive. Public transportation might be an option and you may not even own a car. Shopping will be different, with more stores, more variety, and more upscale options.

Cultural events will be much more at hand, like performance theaters, live entertainment, concerts, and movie theaters. Many single people feel their chances of meeting a mate will be better in the big city where the population is greater. More restaurants and fine dining are available. You may be closer to a major airline hub, making travel more convenient and cheaper.

You could be working at multiple hospitals and bigger hospitals. You are likely to have all the subspecialties available for consultation. You may not know everyone on the hospital staff in a larger hospital.

## Small town

Small towns have a different feel than larger cities in regard to practicing medicine. Here, you will live a slower life and can buy a very nice house, near everything, for much less money. Things cost less in general, but a few things might be more as it took more to get them to your location. Shopping might be farther away if you are after the finer things, but most small towns have all the essentials and you can usually find what you need.

You will experience more open space and peace and quiet. You are more likely to feel good about letting your children walk to school. You often have less crime, cleaner air, and outdoor activities could be right outside your doorstep. Your commute to work will be shorter and thus you will have much more free time to spend with your family.

You might make a smaller income, but costs are less. You could even make a higher income if they are in need of your specialty and are willing to pay a premium to get you.

The medical staff will be smaller and you are likely to know everyone. Patients will run into you at the store and thank you. You might have taken care of multiple people in the same family. In a smaller community, you could be one of the highest earners in town and become a very influential person—a big fish in a small pond.

All the specialties will not be represented in the smaller community and you may have to send some cases away to a bigger city to see a specialist. If you don't want to see the complicated stuff, this can be a bonus. You are less likely to work at multiple hospitals as there may only be one available. With a smaller group of doctors, competition tends to be less as there is usually more than enough work. Fewer doctors, though, means more days on call, but the call will be lighter.

If you make an error in choosing where to live, and become a country mouse in the city or a city mouse in the country, you will likely be unhappy. I know of several doctors who have made this mistake and forked over a lot of money to move to a new practice, as described in the previous chapter. Usually they moved within the first four years—when they could least afford it—after they realized they (or their spouse) were not going to get used to the life.

Don't find yourself in the wrong-sized town, or in the wrong-climate town. Do you like shoveling snow, or dealing with hurricanes?

## LOOK AT THE BIG PICTURE

Where do you see yourself in five, ten, or fifteen years? It's important to know this before you begin your final year of training, when you start searching for your first job. Write down your goals.

Goal setting on paper is a key difference between those who succeed and those who don't. If you are married, do this together. Get a clear understanding of where you are headed and how you are going to get there, otherwise you might never arrive.

If you are married and your spouse wants to work, take this into account. For example, if your spouse is an oceanographer, you will need to look for coastal towns that can accommodate you both. One or the other of you may need to sacrifice your career goals, as there may not be a place for both of your careers in some locations. One doctor I know married an attorney from another country. She can't practice law in the US and he can't practice medicine in her country. Someone has to give. Usually both careers can be accommodated, though, if you think it through ahead of time. Finding that sweet spot is key to your success.

Understanding what you are after and finding it the first time will save a lot of time and money. Picking the wrong job will lead to another round of interviewing and moving, which can be a huge expense in both money and stress. Reevaluate your goals at least on an annual basis, since life is fluid and subject to change. Goals may change with time. Things you thought were important last year may not be so important anymore.

Life is too short to spend time floundering around wondering what you want to do. Pick your path early, begin your journey in the right direction, and you will enjoy the adventure.

**DR. ROLEX** chose the big city life where she could find a variety of the exciting things she liked to do. Research was not her thing, so she didn't interview at any academic centers. She was not too concerned with who her partners would be, since she intended to be an employee of the hospital. The employment model seemed to suit her best, as she didn't want to bother with all the details of running a practice. She took a job with the hospital offering the highest salary and quickly spent her $50,000 sign-on bonus.

The hospital was a busy one and she hit the ground running. She worked a long five-day workweek and seldom made it home for dinner. The weekends were taken up with studying for boards. She seemed busier than she wanted to be, but felt it necessary to get started on the right foot. Her husband began to express concern about the number of hours she was working and the lack of time they spent together. It seemed just like residency.

Her partners didn't turn out to be what she expected. They mostly kept to themselves and each was busy doing their own thing, and they let the hospital run the practice. She had hoped for more guidance from them, since she was fresh out of residency. After three years with no improvement, she started the interview process again and found a better job. The second time, she paid more attention to evaluating her partners and the expected working conditions. Her house didn't sell quickly, the kids had to change schools again, and packing up the house for the move was hard on everyone. She is happier with the new job, but the ordeal was taxing on her and her marriage.

**DR. TIMEX** chose to look for a clinical partnership in a small town. She wanted a slower lifestyle, and the small town she chose seemed to be the right fit. The kids could walk to school every day, and she wouldn't have to waste time commuting. She took great care in interviewing her partners to be sure they all shared a similar philosophy on life. Each of the partners valued their time at home and worked well together to give each other protected time off, which she liked.

This job was not the best salary she was offered, but it seemed a good fit for her priorities and goals. She put the $50,000 sign-on bonus in the bank as a savings cushion, which was a pleasant new experience. She was able to be home almost every night for dinner—except when an occasional urgent problem with a patient interfered.

She enjoyed the mentorship her senior partners provided. They were very interested in her success, and helped her when she asked. She began to learn from them the important concepts needed to run a private practice. The job turned out to be all she hoped for and she has no plans to leave.

# LEARN FROM THE DOCTORS

Dr. Rolex used what she learned from the first job to find a better fit with the second, but was forced to move again, and now she is starting over. She likes her children's school; she's happy with her choice to live in the big city, but with the working hours and her long commute, she doesn't see her family as much as she'd like. With the extra expenses incurred by the move, they had to cancel their vacation for the year.

Dr. Timex is well on her way to building a great reputation and great relationships with her partners. She is happy with her schedule. She hasn't had to change jobs or move, saving considerable expense.

As you encounter Dr. Rolex and Dr. Timex throughout the book, notice how their lifestyle and career decisions affect their overall financial status and job satisfaction.

# Chapter 3

# FINDING YOUR JOB

## WHERE ARE THE JOBS?

Now that you have a better idea what your dream job looks like, how do you find it? As you read earlier, I cold-called practices in the region I had determined I wanted to live. This is probably the best method if you have a fixed geographical location in mind. Many doctors who are looking for a new partner don't advertise. They use word of mouth and contacts with other doctors.

Call or write the medical staff offices of hospitals in the areas you identify, and ask if they know of anyone looking for a new doctor in your specialty. Usually the people working in the medical staff office are very personable. If you ask them about the medical community, they are a wealth of knowledge. If your specialty doesn't work with the hospital, such as dentists or chiropractors, call or write the practices you find on an Internet search in your chosen location.

Where I practiced, we had surgical residents spend their fourth year of training with us. We got to know the residents and they got to know us and the town. There are now three surgeons in town who were residents with us first. This is a good way to land a job. If you have selected someplace you would like to work, take an elective rotation with that practice so you can get to know them. Anything you do to lengthen the courtship period will be beneficial.

Ask your mentors if they know of anyone looking for a new partner. Many of them know of openings and can make an introduction for you. When I was interviewing, one of my future partners trained at the same residency I did. His main research during my interview was to call the chief of surgery at the residency, whom he trusted, and ask him about my abilities. Who you know can play a big role in your future.

If you haven't identified a geographical location, you can search the ads in the back of journals in your specialty for available jobs. Physician recruiting organizations or locum tenens companies also have lists of people and hospitals looking for new doctors. You can find them with a quick Internet search. Their fees are usually paid by the organization you will be joining. Just remember their goal is to connect you with any job, not necessarily the right job.

Go to local and national meetings and introduce yourself to people you might like to work with, or who live in an area you might like to live. Name tags often reveal where they live. Use your contacts on social media for introductions. There are numerous places to find the perfect job, once you know what you want.

# THE INTERVIEW TRIP

Once you have made a connection with a potential employer, they will do some preliminary background checking on you. If they are satisfied, they will want an interview. Be sure you do your homework on them before going for the interview. Don't spend your valuable time interviewing for a job you won't like. Do some preliminary Internet searching on the facilities, the town, and your potential partners.

## Evaluate potential colleagues in your specialty

Before committing to traveling for an interview, make a few phone calls and talk with your potential future partners to assure your compatibility. Also contact those in your specialty who will not be in your practice group. It is surprising how many people show up in town as a new hire who have never communicated with the only other person in their specialty. Talking to your future "competitor" is important. Will they share call with you? Are they on good terms with the hospital? Is there enough work in town for the both of you? Is the hospital trying to put them out of business and take over? You should know these things before committing to the interview.

I know of one orthopedic surgeon who was recruited by a hospital that was trying to monopolize the orthopedics in town, but didn't share this information with the candidate. The administrators told him he would be the only joint specialist in town. He learned of the competing joint specialist by accident during the interview, and was suddenly no longer interested in the job. He wasted an interview trip by not doing his homework. An Internet search for orthopedic surgeons could have given him enough information to reject this interview invitation. He also didn't want to work for anyone who would try to deceive him.

## Let the interviewer pay for the trip

When you think you have a match and are ready to go for the tour, the interviewer should pay for the interview trip. You are a poor resident and they should cover the cost for you and your spouse, if you are married. It is important for you both to meet the people and the town together. They will usually set the agenda. If the medical staff is small, do your best to meet everyone, but when the medical staff is large, that will not be possible. If you are a family practitioner and there are 50 others in town, you can't meet them all. Be sure to meet the key ones, such as those you will work with directly and those who are chairs of key committees like the medical executive committee.

## Evaluate the location

Be sure some time is allotted to tour the town and look at some houses in your budget range. Spend a couple of hours with a real estate agent looking over the area and viewing some neighborhoods, houses, and schools. Check out the housing rental market. Visit the churches in your faith and look into the recreation of interest to you. If you plan to be a frequent flyer, is the airport close enough and will it meet your needs?

# GOOD PARTNERS ARE KEY

Whether you choose to become an owner in a private practice or clinic, or an employee in a hospital, your new partners are the most important factor in choosing your new job. A partnership is a very special relationship. Senior partners mentor junior partners. You cover each other's patients. When you leave town, you are entrusting your practice to them. You socialize together. You may co-own a business. The relationship must have mutual respect, trust, encouragement, and a willingness to help each other. It is a lot like a marriage, only the courtship is shorter. It's important that you like and respect your future partners. Their reputation will spill over onto you, so it better be a good one.

### Coworkers are partners too

It's interesting to hear young doctors dismiss this relationship's importance, especially if employed by a hospital. Many assume if the relationship isn't one of *real* partners sharing a practice, it doesn't matter if you don't like each other. That couldn't be further from the truth. Even as co-employees, you will still need the relationship to work. You will be assisting each other, taking care of each other's patients, and bouncing cases off each other for advice.

A hard and nonnegotiable rule should be: if you don't like one of the doctors in the group, keep looking. As you can see, the choice of a new partner, especially your first one, is very important. If you don't pick well, you will dread going to work each day. Life can become miserable.

A good partnership is like gold. Pay close attention and choose wisely, and you will have a thriving, lifelong relationship.

## THE INTERVIEW

The following list highlights critical components of the relationships you will have with other doctors, as coworkers or partners. Whether you are interviewing for a hospital job or in a large partnership, keep these concepts in mind during the interview. Never forget you are also interviewing *them* to see if they are a good fit for *you*.

## Pay attention to initial impressions

You and your future partners will be on your best behavior. If you don't like something during this phase, unlike wine, it will not improve with time. Your dating period may only be some phone calls, emails, and a dinner party—pretty short courtship. Then once you commit, like in a marriage, you will need to do your best to make it work.

## Consider financial goals and perspectives

Having a similar spending pattern is important in any partnership. If your business partner wants to remodel the office every five years to keep up with the times and you would rather take the money as income to pay off your debts, this may cause conflict. If you are credentialed to do ultrasounds and would like to incorporate it into the practice, but your partner or your hospital employer doesn't want to fork out the $40,000 for the ultrasound machine you need, there may be disagreement.

Sometimes in a partnership, the senior partner may be financially very well off, while you are only at the start of your earning years. His ideas of what constitutes a major expenditure may not be the same as yours. If he starts talking about each of you ponying up $100,000 to set up a colonoscopy suite in the office, you may not be able to keep up.

## Understand shared resources and priorities

Do your new partners share well and play nice together? You will have to share office space and staff with them. Is there enough room for you in the facilities and in the schedule? If the office has only six exam rooms, and your partner gets four of them and you can have two, where will you be in two years when you both have a full practice? Will your partner give up one of the rooms for you? Is the staff already fully utilized and dreading adding another doctor to the load? If so, are they planning to add more staff when you arrive? Will you be sharing a nurse?

One group I know shared a nurse, and one of the doctors did a lot of procedures in the office and the other didn't. The nurse was required to be in the room with the procedure and was therefore not available for the other doctor. This caused some conflict over who gets the nurse. They needed another nurse but were unwilling to hire one. Such a relationship may not last long.

## Look for equal call sharing

Taking call will be a big burden. Is it shared equally, or is there a senior partner who won't take call anymore but expects to be treated as an equal partner? Both the good and the bad need to be shared equally. You might be expecting every fourth night call, only to find one of the partners is retiring when you arrive, and another will be going off the call schedule. Suddenly your one-in-four call becomes every other night.

## Look for a mentor

As a young doctor, you will benefit from guidance. You need a mentor. Jumping from trainee to attending is a big leap in responsibility. There's a lot of room for growth in the first five years of practice. Will your future partners help you along until you have enough experience to feel confident?

I saw one practice where the two existing partners were always in the office together and took the same day off. They wanted the new junior partner to work in the office using the existing holes in the schedule. The new partner would never have a senior partner in the office for advice. Neither of the senior partners was willing to change their long-standing schedule to accommodate a mentorship role. The junior partner was always working solo. After a few months, one of the senior partners gave in and changed his schedule to accommodate and mentor his new partner. If your partners aren't interested in your growth and success, look elsewhere.

## Look for equal ownership

If you are joining a private practice, be sure their intention is for you to become an equal partner. I know of one private practice where the senior partner owns 51% of the practice and the rest of the partners share the other 49%. Income is based on production but ownership is not equal. The senior partner wanted to maintain total control of the practice. He was not really searching for junior partners, he wanted minions. In such a situation, he can never be outvoted. He's making it clear the practice belongs to him and you are working for him, but he will share the profits with you. If you encounter a situation like this, keep looking. Don't enter into a partnership unless all the partners are on equal terms. All for one, and one for all.

## Understand how expenses are split

This is often a sore spot in a partnership since everyone is not in the same situation. The doctor near retirement who wants to cut back thinks she should not have to pay her equal share of the expenses, but wants to keep her share of the income. Just because someone cuts back to half time doesn't mean the expenses attributed to them also decrease. The rent doesn't go down. This reality is what makes it hard for a doctor to work part-time. Similarly, if new equipment only benefits one person, maybe that person should shoulder the cost. For example, if the new doctor coming in wants to do ultrasounds and keep all the billings for reading them, then the rest of the partners shouldn't split the cost of the ultrasound machine. The expenses and the income should be treated the same.

## Listen to your spouse's impression

What does your spouse think of each of the partners and their spouses? It may not seem relevant, but your spouse's opinion should count. I remember interviewing for a practice when I was starting my job search, and my wife did not like one of the wives she met at the interview dinner. I mistakenly felt it was no big deal, as we would not be hanging out with them and I was not going to be partners with the wives anyway. But spouses are not isolated; they share philosophies with the doctor who is your potential colleague. If your spouse is sensing trouble at this point, listen carefully to their intuition.

## Evaluate the reputation of the doctors, staff, and the practice in general

What is the reputation of the group in the community? You will be working hard to establish a great reputation and if they already have such a reputation, you get a big head start. Other doctors will assume the group would only hire a new partner that measures up to their existing standards. If the group doesn't have a good reputation, you will be starting in a hole and you may not be able to get out. Think twice about joining a group with a bad reputation. Look them up online. Check out their social media sites. See what the online rating services have to say (but take them with a grain of salt—as any anonymous rating system is susceptible to abuse, and the unhappy patients tend to post more). Ask the nurses what they think.

## Share charitable and philanthropic values

Does the group do any kind of charity work beyond taking patients who cannot pay? If this is important to you, find partners with a like mind. One group I know allows each doctor to go on a third world mission trip. If your future partners are opposed to you missing your share of call to go on a mission trip, it may be difficult for you to ever fulfill this desire. And, if this is not your desire, you may not want to join a group that's committed to third world missions. Do they donate to charities? Do you support the same charities?

## Share similar religious values

If you are interviewing with business partners in a privately-owned practice, religion may be an issue. You may not want to be partners with people who share a very different religious philosophy from you. Otherwise, when you want to put up a picture in the waiting room of the Dalai Lama and your partner wants a picture of Jesus, there may be some strife. You don't need to attend the same church, but make sure you are compatible.

## Evaluate their educational mindset

You are fresh out of training and have been working with the latest technology and ideas. Are your potential partners open to learning something new from you? Will they help you pass your boards by giving you some time off to study or sharing their study material?

Sharing educational material is very helpful and keeps expenses down. If one partner goes to a meeting, will they come back and share anything new they picked up? Gaining the pearls from a meeting you didn't attend saves a lot of money, as each of you can go to different meetings and gain knowledge faster.

## Understand hiring motivations

It is important to know why the practice is seeking a new doctor. There are many reasons and some of them are not so good. Is the practice overworked and in desperate need of someone to come in and take some of the load? If so, you will hit the ground running. Is one of the partners looking to retire and give you all their patients? Is a partner leaving the practice? If so, is it on good terms? The office staff may be a better source for this question, especially if there were adverse reasons for the partner's exit. Are they being proactive and hiring a new doctor before they reach the breaking point? Is the hospital hiring doctors in an attempt to corner the market and put the competition out of business? If so, there will be doctors in town who resent your coming. Not a good environment in which to cut your teeth.

## Evaluate the facilities

Is the hospital staffed and supplied well? Do the doctors in the other specialties say good things about the hospital? How is the hospital doing financially? Is it making money and constantly buying new equipment, or barely getting by and may close its doors soon if something big doesn't happen? Is the hospital a critical access hospital (CAH) and if so, is it often at capacity? If the hospital is always full, your patients may need to go elsewhere or you may not be able to do elective procedures. Is there a surgery center? Who owns it? Can you become an owner? Will it accommodate your specialty? Is the hospital a partner or a competitor? Is the office staffed for your needs? Are there enough exam rooms and support staff?

## Ask about major upcoming changes to the practice or institution

Are there any big changes coming down the pike? If the hospital is changing status or being bought out, you might not like the new owners. Is the group about to build a new building and expects you to help pay for it? That might hurt your ability to pay off your student loans in a timely fashion. Are they about to transition to a new electronic medical record (EMR) system the month after you arrive? Is the hospital about to expand or rebuild?

## Take notes about the details

When you leave the interview, you should have a good feel for the people and the town. Take notes immediately about what you liked and didn't like. These will be important to compare when you come down to your two favorite sites and need a tiebreaker.

# Chapter 4

# NEGOTIATING YOUR CONTRACT

When you get the offer for the job you want, get ready to make it the best it can be by negotiating the important terms of your contract. The purpose of a contract is to assure all parties understand what is expected.

Make sure everything you want is there before signing. Once you sign, you will be expected to perform as it states. One of the biggest grievances people had with Congress when they adopted the Affordable Care Act in 2010, was they passed it without understanding what it said. It was more than a third of a million words long, and most members of Congress had not read it. Comments were made that they needed to pass it first, and then they would figure out what it meant.

Don't begin your practice like that. Understand what is expected of you and make sure everyone understands what you plan to deliver. Then deliver more than expected.

This is one time in your life when you may have significant negotiating power. They are recruiting you because they need you. When you have something they want, you have negotiating power. Now is the time to ask for benefits. Once you sign a contract and begin to work for your employer, negotiating power drops significantly. Take advantage of this small window of opportunity to get what you want. Don't be a deer staring into the headlights of a huge salary and sign-on bonus and forget everything else.

## ATTORNEY REVIEW

The contract you sign for your first job out of residency may be the most valuable one in your life. If your salary is $250,000 a year and you plan to work 30 years, that's a $7.5 million contract, without counting benefits—a pretty big deal. Get your own attorney to look over the contract with you. His fee is nothing compared to the contract size. Don't take this lightly. The other party who drew up the contract had it prepared by an attorney who was on their side. Make sure to balance it with an attorney on your side.

## WHAT TO INCLUDE IN YOUR CONTRACT

There are a myriad of benefits available for the asking. You usually will not get everything you want, but being prepared to negotiate helps. Write down your top priorities. Of course, the largest benefit is salary, and everyone wants as much as they can get. Sometimes the other party is not willing to give what you want on this one. They may be working under some constraints, but you can make up for it with benefits. Benefits can be extremely valuable to you and may not matter much to the other party, especially if they are concentrating on getting you at a certain salary. Always remember the arrangement needs to be a win-win deal. Both parties should have their needs met.

## Salary and bonus

There's a lot more to salary than the number. How your pay is determined makes a big difference. Straight salary, not tied to any production numbers, is the easiest to understand. Most contracts have some sort of production bonus written in. Make sure the bonus is something easy to calculate. One friend of mine got to the end of the year looking for his bonus, only to find the hospital didn't have any way of showing him how the calculations were made. Not being able to see the calculations made him feel he was being cheated. Maybe he was being cheated, or maybe he wasn't—but he doesn't know, and that impacted his job satisfaction. The point is to avoid this by making sure the calculations are transparent and easy to understand.

Something simple, like a multiplication of total relative value units (RVUs) generated, can be very easy to understand. Another would be some figure over a threshold of RVUs of production.

Always be sure figures are based on your production and not on what is collected, or net profit. If you join a partnership and your income is based on collections, your senior partner, who already has a referral base, can take all the paying patients and leave you with the nonpaying patients, and he'll get more pay for the same work. Every gallbladder you remove or history and physical (H&P) you perform should be worth the same value, whether or not the patients have insurance. If bonuses are based on net profits, it's easy to keep adding expenses and never show a profit. What you are after is something fair for everyone and easy to understand.

## Vacation

This is a very important item, so don't skimp here. Healthcare professionals don't stop working when the clock strikes five. We take work home. We wake up at night to a pager and can't get back to sleep. We worry about outcomes even when we are not working. Lots of nights and weekends are spent away from our families. In short, we work a lot of hours at a high level of stress and many of those hours are not on the clock. Time for recharging is very important—and most administrators don't understand this.

Try and get at least six weeks of real vacation each year. If you don't ask for it on the original contract, it will be hard to get later. However much vacation you think you need, you will need more. In a salary-based system this may be hard to get, as your employer wants you there, producing profits for them. You will be more productive if you have a chance to periodically recharge than you will if you get burned out.

In a fully production-based system, they shouldn't care how much vacation you take, since when you are gone and not producing, your pay will decrease as well. I worked under this kind of arrangement for eighteen years, and took eight to twelve weeks off each year. Get as much time off as you can negotiate, even if it means dropping your salary to compensate. Your sanity will thank me later.

## Time and compensation for continuing education

You will be required by the hospital and your licensing board to take a certain amount of continuing education each year. You may be required to take special classes on a recurring basis, like Advanced Trauma Life Support (ATLS), Advanced Cardiac Life Support (ACLS), Pediatric Advanced Life Support (PALS), and others. These courses are not vacation, so you will need some additional time off to accommodate them. Two weeks should do. I know a hospital employee who was required to attend a course to use a new piece of equipment. When he requested his final week of vacation that year he was told he had no vacation time left. The hospital had booked his trip for the required course against his vacation time. Continuing education courses are not vacations, especially when they are required.

There should also be a provision for them to pay for some of this education. You should be able to submit your expenses for reimbursement up to a maximum amount, say $2,500–$5,000. They require it, so they should help pay.

## Sick/family leave

There should be a provision for sick leave. This tends to accrue as you work. One to two weeks a year is good. It's best if this time isn't considered vacation. Some contracts combine all your time off into one category, personal time. They don't care if it is sick leave, educational, or vacation, it all counts the same. This is OK, as long as the total time adds up to what you should have in all these areas. If they use such a system and allow you only three weeks off a year, it will not be enough to keep you healthy. Be sure you have accounted for family/maternity leave. You are likely to need this at some time and it is better if you spell it out early.

## Malpractice insurance

Be sure the contract specifies what type and how much malpractice insurance you have. If they use a "claims made" policy, determine who will be responsible for the extended reporting endorsement, commonly known as a tail, when you leave. If it is a partnership, you will likely be responsible for your own tail. If you work for a hospital, try to have them pay the tail when you leave. If the hospital is self-insured, you won't have to worry about a tail. The two types of insurance, claims made and occurrence, will be covered later.

## Exit terms

It seems like a funny time to start talking about leaving as you're agreeing to your first job, but it's important to lay out the foundation for this now. Be sure the exit strategy is spelled out in the contract. At some point in the future, you or one of your partners will either find a new job or retire. The time to spell out the terms of this is now, while it is not an issue. Be sure any terms for a buyout are easy to understand and the same for you as for the senior partners.

Some practices have a mandatory retirement age and some don't. What if your partner is beyond performing well at his advanced age but won't retire; is there a provision for removal? What are the terms for dismissal for cause, when you do something bad and get fired? Is there a notice period for you to leave or for them to let you go without cause? Ask for at least 90 days—the more the better.

## Retirement plan

When are you eligible to participate in the company retirement plan? Most will have a waiting period, such as January first after you have worked for one full year. Will the company match your funds? Is there a vesting period, where if you leave before a certain time, they will take back their matching funds? As part of your due diligence, you should know what kinds of investment options are available in the plan, although those won't likely be negotiable.

## Pay for being on call/working extra shifts

Taking call is a great burden. Getting paid to shoulder that burden certainly seems fair and could offset the time you lose from your elective practice, your family, and your nights and weekends off. Be sure they are compensating you fairly for the amount of call they are requiring.

If you do shift work in an emergency department or as a hospitalist and you are contracted to do a certain number of shifts per month, can you take extra shifts? You can substantially boost your income by taking additional shifts.

## Day off

Ask for one unscheduled day each workweek, a day off. This day allows you some time to catch up or plan non-work-related appointments. My day off was Tuesday; I was able to make plans knowing I would have some free time and never be on call Tuesdays. My wife and I were able to take weekly classes. I could get a haircut, have my teeth cleaned, or schedule other appointments without fear of having to cancel them.

I officially had the day off, but there were always things to do— an operation that had to be worked in, a backlog of charts, administrative paperwork, catching up on journals, hospital committee work, etc. Having a day during the week to help with these items makes it more likely you will stay caught up and have the weekend free. These things are included in your duties and you shouldn't have to do them on your weekend off.

## Moving expenses

It is reasonable to expect your employer to pay for your moving expenses. They should cover actual costs, up to a set amount. Most residents don't have the money to pay for the move.

## Sign-on bonus

Depending on how desperately a practice needs you, they may offer a sign-on bonus to get you to pick them over the competition. This is a great perk. It can be used to help get you established in your house, buy furniture, replace the resident car you've been nursing along, or even pay down some of your debt. If you get this money, don't blow it. Use it sparingly and wisely—$50,000 to get started is very helpful. It also makes a great emergency fund.

## Royalties

If you are planning on working at a university and are an entrepreneur, be sure you spell out who owns your work. Some places feel if you invent something or write a book while they are paying your salary, it belongs to the university. I don't agree. Some of the work will be done on your own time and some of the work will be done on their time. Giving them full ownership is not fair. You don't want to come up with an idea as revolutionary as the Fogarty catheter and get nothing financially from the process because the university claims they own it.

## Loan repayment

Postgraduate training is getting absurdly expensive and many young doctors are drowning in debt. Negotiating some kind of loan repayment plan into your contract can be very rewarding. Many places will be happy to do this as it might give them an edge over the competition, and they know it's on your mind.

Be careful with the forgivable loan, where the employer will give you a loan and every year you work they will forgive part of it. This is good as long as you stay with them. If you leave before the period specified in the contract, you will have to pay back the loan. If you used the money for something other than paying down your loans, you just went further into debt.

## Health insurance

You want to have good health insurance for the whole family, not just you. Many employers are scaling back health insurance to save money as the cost continues to rise. They may only offer it free to the employee and you have to pay the premiums for the rest of the family. Ideally you get the whole family covered with no premiums paid by you. They may also have a high deductible plan, meaning you pay for the first $5,000 and they pay the rest. If so, you may be able to have a health savings account (HSA). This is a tax-advantaged account similar to an individual retirement account (IRA), which can only be used for healthcare expenses, but you don't have to wait until you are 59 ½ years old to use it. If you get one, don't use it to pay for anything. Keep putting money in but don't take it out. Use your monthly income to pay for healthcare expenses and use the HSA as another retirement account, a stealth IRA. Don't take anything out until you are retired, and then use it for your healthcare needs when you no longer have a monthly earned income. This allows you to put more money away in a tax-advantaged account.

## Noncompete clause

The contract you sign may include a noncompete clause. No practice or hospital wants to recruit you to become their competitor, so they may include a noncompete clause. This may bar you from practicing within a designated geographic area for a specified period of time, if you should leave their employment. Try to remove this clause, since it is of no benefit to you—only your employer benefits.

If you can't remove it, then be sure the terms are reasonable. They can't tell you not to practice in the entire state, but within twenty miles might be OK. Consider a buyout for this clause, such as: for $50,000 consideration, the clause is void and you can set up your own competing practice. In reality though, the noncompete clause is usually not an issue, since wanting out of the contract often means you also want to leave the area.

## OTHERS

There will be several sections of lawyer talk in the contract, such as arbitration and waiver. Don't be too concerned about these sections but do read and understand them. The following is a list of other topics you may want to discuss. Some will be in the contract and some will not:

### Working conditions

✓ What are the office hours?

✓ Do you make rounds on your day off?

✓ Are the weekends free if you are not on call?

✓ Who is covering your after-hours patient calls, you or the person on call?

✓ Is the office open on Saturdays?

✓ Which holidays are observed?

✓ Who makes the call schedule?

✓ How often must you take call?

✓ How are patients distributed?

✓ If you need operating room (OR) time, is time available or is the schedule full?

✓ How is OR time assigned to the new doctors?

## Partnership buy-in

✓ If a partnership, when will you buy in?

✓ How will the buy-in work and how much will it cost?

✓ Will you be buying the building?

✓ How will the building value be determined?

## Office and equipment

✓ Will you own, rent, or be supplied an office?

✓ Who supplies the personal office furniture?

## Other benefits and income sources

✓ Are there any ancillary businesses you can participate in, like a surgery center or lab?

✓ Are there any other perks, such as a gym membership?

✓ If you bring a new procedure to the practice, will they support it?

✓ If you eventually want to work part-time, will they support it?

✓ Will they provide an automobile allowance?

✓ Will they pay for your dues and subscriptions?

## Other obligations

✓ Will you be required to attend any monthly or annual meetings?

✓ Are there any social/learning events, like a journal club?

✓ Are you expected to make any lectures or presentations?

✓ Will you have any research obligations?

✓ Will you have committee obligations?

✓ Are there any students or residents you will be teaching?

## Staff and other resources

✓ Will you have a physician's assistant or nurse practitioner working with you?

✓ Do they provide any special electronic medical records training?

The more issues you address before your first day of work, the less likely you are to have misunderstandings. Spending time thinking about what you desire from the practice and prioritizing it will put you in a much better negotiating position. You should be fully aware of what items are nonnegotiable for you and on what items you are willing to compromise.

*You are more likely to get what you want when you know what you want.*

# Chapter 5

# PREPARING FOR YOUR FIRST DAY

## STATE LICENSING

Once you have established where you will be working, you must immediately start the process of getting a license to practice medicine in that state. If you are lucky, you will be practicing in the state where you did your training and already have a license. Every state has different rules as to what they require. In some states it is a quick and easy process, but in others it is quite an ordeal.

When I retired from my private practice and started doing locums work, I noticed the same states kept coming up with opportunities. When I inquired as to why the other states never had an opening, I learned the licensing process is too cumbersome in those states. In states with a slower licensing process, they offered the job to someone who already had the required license. It can take up to six months to get a license in some states.

You may have to appear for a personal interview, in some states; in others, they only look at your paperwork. In some states, the board of medical examiners only meets quarterly. If you turn in your application one month before the meeting and they are unable to get all the needed verifications before the meeting, your file will not go before the board until the next meeting—in three months.

Some states require a valid address in their state before you can start applying for a license. Therefore, you can't start the process ahead of getting a job. The idea of getting a license early because you know you want to spend the rest of your life in that particular state will not work.

Since you cannot get any hospital privileges until you have the proper state licenses, you should start this process early. For this reason, you can't wait until two months before graduation to line up your job.

Some states do not accept your DEA (Drug Enforcement Agency) number as the only requirement to prescribe narcotics. They have their own additional system. After you have a license, then you can apply to prescribe narcotics—another delay in the process. Obtain your DEA number early in your training, so as to not cause even more delay.

You may have to complete special continuing medical education (CME) training, in some states, before submitting your application. You will need time to find a course, take it, and get a certificate—another chunk of time.

## HOSPITAL CREDENTIALING AND PRIVILEGING

Hospital credentialing and privileging is also a lengthy process. You must apply and have all your supporting documents in place before the file moves on through the committee process, even if you were a resident there for the last three years. Your application will pass through several committees, each meeting only once a month: the credentials committee, the medical executive committee, and then the hospital board. Some hospitals may speed up the process if there is a legitimate time crunch, otherwise it will take a while.

Get started at the same time you apply for the state license. They will not pass your paperwork through the committees before you have your license, but there is a lot of work to be done before that anyway. They will need to contact your school and have documents forwarded to them. They will need your references and test scores. The sooner you can start this process, the better. Often, getting peer references holds up the process the longest. Contact your peers and remind them your application can't proceed without their input. And remember this when you are asked to be a reference for someone else—get on it right away and don't hold them up.

When asking for privileges, you will find two kinds of systems: lumpers and splitters—those who group (lump) related items together, and those who don't (splitters). The lumpers use what is called core privileges. For example, you apply for everything an internal medicine doctor might be expected to do by checking one box, for internal medicine core. Reading EKGs, for example, would be included.

The splitters have every single item listed and if you are a surgeon, this is a chore. Instead of one check mark for all privileges a general surgeon would need, they list every operation you could do. Taking out an appendix is a separate privilege from taking out a gallbladder.

The splitting system is problematic if you are not sure you want to do something. Knowing that it's easier to drop a privilege than it is to ask for it later, ask for everything you are qualified to do, even if you don't think you will do it. If, for example, you can do thyroidectomies but don't intend to do them, ask for the privilege anyway. You really don't know what the practice will be like and what referrals you will have until you start working. If it turns out the local ENT doctor is not in good standing with his peers and you can do thyroids, you might suddenly have a booming business as a thyroid surgeon.

If you didn't ask for the privilege in your initial appointment, and you find this out later and want to go back and add thyroidectomy to your privileges, you will need to provide proof of knowledge and experience. You will need to account for why you didn't think you had the experience for it when you initially applied, and now you suddenly have the experience. It is much easier to get the privileges on your first application.

The same thing holds true for changing jobs. You will have a hard time getting a privilege at your new job that you didn't have at the old one.

Privilege lumpers have their problems as well. I took a locums job at a critical access hospital that had core general surgery privileges. I did an amputation on the weekend and on Monday there was trouble. It seems the last general surgeon did not do amputations, only the orthopedic specialist did. The hospital did not consider amputations one of my core privileges. I, on the other hand, had done many amputations and considered it one of my core privileges; at least it was in my last hospital. It all worked out in the end when they learned I had ample experience, but it did cause some problems with differing expectations of what was included in the core privileges.

Taking call for the emergency department of the hospital will often be a requirement. To have privileges, you must take call. Some specialties are now covered by full-time employees at the hospital, which may relieve the call burden for those specialties.

For example, if the hospital employs a hospitalist team, the internal medicine doctors in town might not have to take call for the hospital. You will still have to take call for your practice, though. If the hospitalists are all internal medicine doctors, the pediatricians may still need to take call at the hospital. Don't let this requirement force you into an unreasonable amount of call. Just because you come on as the only pediatrician doesn't mean you should have to be on call for the hospital 24/7. It is the hospital's responsibility to provide coverage for their emergency department, not yours.

Government regulations currently make the privileging process unduly long and tedious. The worst part, though, is it will only be good for a maximum of two years. Then you have to completely repeat the application process. Many hospitals have their staff bundled together by specialty, so all the family practice doctors reapply on the same month every two years. This makes it easy for the hospital to keep track of when you will need to renew, and spreads out their work more evenly. If you are unlucky enough to get your privileges only eight months before the start of that cycle for your specialty, you will be repeating the whole process in eight months. Don't shoot the messenger and get mad at the people in the medical staff office who are putting you through this; they have no choice. If you make a copy of your application before you turn it in, when they come back in two years, you will already have everything you need to fill out the forms. At least the subsequent applications will be quicker than the first one.

## SPECIAL CREDENTIALS

There are several extra credentials you may need at your new job. There is a good chance you will already have these. They are ACLS, ATLS, PALS, and the like. If your hospital will require you to have an ACLS card before letting you do a colonoscopy and you don't have one yet, you will not be able to do a colonoscopy until you complete the course. Find out what they require and see if you can take care of it before leaving your training.

Some hospitals also require special tests or courses for certain privileges as well. Some have you take a test if you will be providing conscious sedation, for example.

Another time delay is getting approval from all the insurance panels. Each health insurance company will need to approve you before you can see any patients they cover. This should be completed for all insurance companies before your first day of work. Lots more paperwork. If this is not done by the time you start, you will not be paid if you see any patients covered by their policies. Your partners will not be happy if you are not able to take care of *any* patient who walks through the door.

# INSURANCE FOR YOUR NEW LIFE

As you start your practice, you will begin acquiring assets which need protecting. Nothing will financially wipe you out faster than a sudden catastrophe. A $600,000 hospital bill, a $1 million lawsuit, a flood, or a disabling injury could spell disaster. This is the reason for insurance. Without the right insurance in place, you could be totally devastated in a single year.

There are many different types of insurance, but only a few you need. Some of these will be incorporated into your employment contract, such as health and malpractice insurance, and some will need to be purchased separately.

### Malpractice insurance

We all know about this one. It's almost guaranteed you will be sued for malpractice at some time during your career. If you are a neurosurgeon or deliver babies, you can count on being sued multiple times.

There are two types of malpractice insurance: *occurrence* and *claims made*.

Occurrence is the one you want but it's harder to find. This insurance covers you for malpractice that occurred during the time you were insured, whether or not you are still insured, and with no regard to when you are sued. If you had the insurance when you saw the patient—when the event occurred—you are covered.

Claims made is insurance covering you at the time the patient files the claim of malpractice—but you are only covered if you were also insured at the time of the patient encounter. If you change jobs and your insurance company changes, claims made poses a problem. They will not cover you for events that occurred before they started insuring you (a preexisting problem), and they will cover nothing claimed after you stop the policy. To cover a suit for events occurring prior to the policy, you need to buy *nose* coverage. To cover for patients suing you after the policy ends you will need to buy a *tail*. Do you smell a rat?

Tail coverage can be very expensive, as in double your annual insurance premium. Be aware of the type of insurance your employer uses. If it is claims made, the contract should state who pays the tail. Hopefully, not you. If you change employers, you may be able to negotiate for your new employer to buy a nose instead of you buying a tail for the old policy. Either one will cover the transition. Your best shot at this is including it as part of your contract during that magical period of contract negotiation.

### Auto insurance

You also need this insurance and in some states it is required. Buy large policy limits for liability, as once a victim realizes a doctor was the driver in an accident, they might feel they can get a bit more from you. Raising your deductible will help you lower your rates. Ask to see the rates for each level of deductible and make a comparison before deciding.

## Homeowners insurance

This is another place to save on premiums by raising your deductible. It's important to understand that insurance companies are in the business of collecting premiums, not paying claims. Therefore, they will not insure your stuff against theft if it is likely to get stolen. Go figure. For example, your coverage might be limited to $1,000 for jewelry. If you have lots of nice jewelry and a burglar hits your house and feels he needs it more than you do, your insurance will only cover the first $1,000. If you want more coverage, you have to insure each item separately. I learned this the hard way. Same thing if you collect art: insure each piece. If the burglar steals your couch, they will cover you for that. Be sure the insurance salesman is very clear and you fully understand what is covered, what is not, and what has limits. Big things like floods, hurricanes, earthquakes, and tornados might not be covered and they are the things that can wipe you out.

## Renters insurance

This is what you get for those first few years before you buy a house. It is much cheaper than homeowners insurance, because they are not insuring the building against loss. This insurance will cover your stuff if it gets stolen—your couch anyway—and will cover you for liability if someone gets hurt at your place.

## Disability insurance

You are more likely to become disabled during your working years than to die. If you do become disabled, the government will pay you some disability money, but it won't be nearly enough to cover the lifestyle you have established.

This insurance comes in two types, *own occupation* and *general* (any occupation). You want to have own occupation if it's available, which will pay you if you can no longer practice your specialty. For example, if a gastroenterologist lost a hand, he couldn't do his own occupation—because endoscopes take two hands—but the insurance company could claim he could still be a general internist, which he is trained for. Under an own occupation policy, he would be covered; under a general policy he might not be.

They will set you up with a policy based on a percentage of your income. If you make $20,000 a month, they will not give you a policy paying $25,000 a month if you couldn't work. That would be too great an incentive to "become" disabled. So once your income skyrockets, then purchase a policy, or get a new one if you already have one in place. Get one that escalates with inflation, and as large a percentage of your income as you can afford.

## Life insurance

The purpose of this insurance is to support the people who are dependent on your income if you die and aren't there to provide for them anymore. This is usually your spouse and children. If you are single, there is no one depending on your income and you do not need life insurance. Don't waste the money. Many agents will try to make you worry about getting a disease and becoming uninsurable in the future, but the odds are way in your favor that this won't happen. Don't buy life insurance until someone else depends on your income.

My wife worked during the first few years of our marriage and she could still take care of herself if I died. After our first child was born, she chose to stay home with him and then they both depended on me for financial support—and so I bought my first life insurance policy. Stick with term insurance and consider a twenty-year level-term policy for an amount to support your spouse and kids through college. The premium cost will stay the same for twenty years, making it easy to include in the budget.

Stay away from any life insurance product wrapped up with an investment, such as universal life. Investments are to make money for your use while you are still alive. Life insurance is for your dependents to live on if you die. Those are opposites—so don't try to combine them. Any type of life insurance combined with an investment serves the function of providing a very nice commission for the one who sold it to you. Those commissions come right out of your pocket. Stick with a term policy and invest your money elsewhere as you see fit. If you play your cards right, after your twenty-year level term policy ends, you will no longer need any life insurance. By then, you should be able to retire, and insurance will no longer be needed to support your family if you die, since your investments will do that.

So how much insurance do you need? This is a lot like the story of *Goldilocks and the Three Bears*. Too little insurance and your family is not covered, and may struggle without your income. Too much, and you waste money on premiums. Just right is what you seek.

If you have calculated your net worth and have a budget, it's not hard to come up with the amount of insurance you need. First, you will want to pay off all your debts. Second, you will need enough money to set up a fund for your dependents to live well by withdrawing four percent of the principle every year. You calculate that by multiplying the annual need by 25. Third, include enough to get your children through college. Add in any special needs, like buying a house if you don't yet have one. Subtract any savings you already have accumulated, and any passive income or government relief you will have.

## Life insurance calculation example

Let's look at an example of a new doctor in the first year of practice whose spouse doesn't work, who has two children and $250,000 in loans, and rents a house. Their annual budgetary need with the loans paid off is $80,000 gross, before taxes. They also have $20,000 in savings and no passive income.

Total outstanding debt = $250,000

Cost of college for the kids = $25,000 per year for each = $200,000

Enough to buy a house for the family = $400,000

Annual budget needs at a 4% withdrawal rate = $80,000 x 25 = $2,000,000

Subtract the savings = -$20,000

The total required = $2,830,000

Based on these numbers, a reasonable amount of life insurance for this family is a $3 million twenty-year level term policy.

## Umbrella insurance

This is not insurance against rain, but a great and inexpensive way to increase your overall insurance coverage. It puts an umbrella over everything. Your insurance company will require you to have your home, car, and any other insured toy, like a motorhome or boat, insured with them before they will provide this. They will also require a high coverage level on these before they will offer an umbrella policy. Then you can add $1 million extra coverage—the umbrella—for a relatively small additional fee. You will be a target as a high income earner, so the extra insurance will more adequately protect your assets.

# TAKE A BREAK

You have spent a significant amount of your life to this point working an insane number of hours per week. You are likely pretty worn out by the end of your training. The gap between finishing your training and starting your new job is a golden opportunity to take a sabbatical or extended vacation.

When I finished my residency, with every other night on call during the final year, I was exhausted. My wife and I had saved up some money during residency, and used it to take three months off before beginning my new job. There will never be a good time to do that once you start working. This will allow you time to get some rest and relaxation, and study for your board exam.

This will require some advanced planning. You will need to have saved enough cash to last until your first paycheck.

Find a way to take this opportunity. I know doctors who have ended training on Friday and started their new job on the other side of the country on Monday. Don't put yourself through that. Take a reasonable amount of time off—it doesn't have to be three months, but at least three weeks, if possible. Get yourself settled into your new house before you start working.

Also, understand the time frame for taking your board certification exam. Some specialties may take the exam right away, while others may not take the exam until after you are in practice for a specified period. Be sure you allot for some intense study time during the months preceding the exam. Boards are difficult to pass without studying. There's some stigma associated with not passing your board exam, so put great effort into passing it the first time.

# Chapter 6

# BUILDING YOUR LIFE AS A DOCTOR

Starting a practice is a very exciting time. All the lean times eating Top Ramen and peanut butter sandwiches have been leading to this. Now you finally have arrived and will start making a great salary. In fact, your income could place you in the top five percent of United States households. You will likely experience an income jump of four to ten times what you were making in residency.

There are great temptations when this happens. Sudden new wealth has a history of damaging the financial well-being of the recipients. We've all heard about lottery winners who end up worse off than they were. Or people who inherit money and their spending decisions ruin their lives. Or professional athletes who sign a contract for $5 million a year for three years, and five years later they are bankrupt and broke. How could they let $15 million slip through their fingers?

# INCREASE YOUR LIFESTYLE GRADUALLY

Your newfound high income will tempt you to buy a big house, new furniture, cars, motorhomes, planes, vacations, jewelry, motorcycles, skis, and the list goes on and on. After spending so much time on a small income or living on borrowed money, when the floodgates open you are tempted to finally get all that you've put off.

Herein lies the peril. You'll want to hold your horses before jumping into an expensive lifestyle. Take a good look at your current situation. If you are like many new doctors, you borrowed your way through medical school, and the interest on those loans is dragging you deeper into debt every day. But don't panic—you can live better now and pay off your loans at the same time, if you prioritize your spending.

Now is the best opportunity you will have in your entire life to establish a firm financial foundation, and move ahead with confidence. If you forge ahead without a plan, you could find yourself in worse shape than you were during training.

Here are some questions to ask yourself when determining how to do this: Do you have all the right insurance in place? Is your debt under control? Do you have six months of living expenses in reserve? Have you set up a plan for your children's education? For your retirement?

It seems premature to be thinking about your retirement, but now is when you set the ball in motion. If you establish a budget that doesn't include everything you need from the beginning, you won't find room to work it in later. If you think you will save the leftover money, you will be in for a shock. There will never be any leftover money. You must fund the necessities first, and then when you run out of money, you miss out on a luxury, not something important.

It's critical that you determine what your spending/saving priorities are. Is it really worth sacrificing the money you would have put into your children's college savings plan to buy a new boat? Is a bigger house worth it, if you have to work an extra ten years because you had too little left for your retirement plan? I'm not saying you can't have the bigger house or the boat at some point, but you should get them only after the important things like debt payments and tax-deductible retirement plans are accounted for. When it is economically prudent to do so.

Remember every jump in lifestyle comes with a set of hidden costs. Bigger houses come with bigger tax bills, higher utility bills, more furniture, and more upkeep. And don't get me started on boats—I know, I had one. They are a hole in the water into which you throw money. You better have a lot of expendable money coming in before you make that move.

Now is when you will set in motion the financial results of all your hard work. Expand your lifestyle in a controlled manner. If you expand your lifestyle too rapidly, borrowing even more money, you will find yourself tied to earning a living. The payments for your lifestyle can get so high that you feel trapped and have to work to keep your head above water. Having to work and wanting to work are two very different things. Don't lose control now, just when the ultimate control is staring you in the face.

When you make a campfire, there are two options. Start with some kindling and keep adding more and bigger pieces to the fire in a controlled fashion until it reaches the size you want. Or, pour a pint of gasoline on the wood and stand back when you toss in the match. With the latter, you will see some fast results and possibly get burned, but the coals will not be as good when the gasoline burns off and you are ready to roast your marshmallows.

Now is the time to set your finances up right. You will have a big influx of money and you are in control of how it will be used. If you don't do it now, you likely will never do it, as a chance like this may not come twice.

Take your time and plan for the wise use of this money. A slow and controlled expansion of your lifestyle will create a lifetime of dividends, and you will become a multimillionaire.

Bad planning now can lead you to becoming a high income earner working paycheck to paycheck. The house you choose can either become a blessing to you and your family or a chain around your ankle, forcing you to keep production up or work extra shifts to pay the bills.

Slow and steady wins the race. You want a good campfire that will last all night so the kids will have fun making s'mores. Shortcuts will usually expose a poorly-laid plan—or no plan.

Several famous people stated this concept:

*"Things which matter most must never be at the mercy of things which matter least."*

**—Johann Wolfgang von Goethe**

*"You gotta make it a priority to make your priorities a priority."*

**—Richie Norton**

*"Put first things first and we get second things thrown in: put second things first and we lose both first things and second things."*

**—C. S. Lewis**

Doctors make very good money. There is no reason for a doctor to struggle financially. Most who do can trace the root of the problem back to the first few financial decisions they made when starting their practice. Most often it was about expanding their lifestyle too rapidly.

If you don't expand your lifestyle too rapidly and remain in control, you can usually get everything you want. You will get it when you can afford it and you will fully understand the cost. You will also have a good handle on what you're giving up when you do make the purchase. You will not need to pay extra for anything—in the form of interest. You will have the money to pay for the lifestyle you seek. Take your time. Do it right the first time. Stay in control and accelerate smoothly.

## DON'T RUSH TO BUY A HOUSE

You will have forces working on you from all angles, trying to get you to immediately purchase a house. During interviews, you might be taken around by a real estate agent to see what housing is available in the area. The agent is unlikely to show you anything in the rental market; he wants to sell you a house. Your new partners will likely own houses and you will want to fit in. The American way is to own a house. Most financial gurus will be leading you to own a house. The government will give you some tax breaks if you buy a house. Your well-meaning friends will tell you you're throwing away money if you rent.

I think you should eventually buy a house, but not right now. Buying and selling houses is expensive and you may need your cash for other things. You are likely to be carrying a huge debt forward from your training. This debt should be addressed in a major way before piling on a mortgage. If you are joining a group in private practice, you will need to prepare for buying your share of the practice. You may need a car soon.

The costs of getting into a new house are high, and your risk of moving soon after you purchase it is also high. Even if you interviewed your partners carefully and made the best choice you could, you may discover after working with them that you don't get along well; they were on their best behavior when you interviewed. You were also on your best behavior, and after the honeymoon period they might not like you. You might not like the town after living there for a while. If you buy a house first thing and something doesn't work out, you will be moving and forced to sell a house you recently purchased.

Many doctors leave their first practice after a very short time for various reasons. There are studies on the rate of physicians trading practices, and they range from 30–70% chance of leaving their first practice within five years. In my own recent experience, eight general surgeons were hired in the last few years in Grants Pass and three of them left within five years (37.5%). Some of those remaining have not yet reached five years and could potentially boost the percentage.

If you happen to be one of those who leave within five years and you are renting a house, it is easier for you to pick up and leave with minimal cost. If you have a house to sell, you might be sorry.

I know several doctors who needed to move from a house they owned only a short time, and the housing market happened to be down. They couldn't sell the house for what they owed and ended up keeping it as a rental. These reluctant landlords now live a long way from their rental, creating additional headaches and frequently losing money on the deal. All would have been fine if they rented when they first came to town and waited to see how things worked out.

Many people who hear this don't believe renting could be cheaper than buying in the short run. I've even heard, "There is a 100% chance you won't profit if you rent." This is based on the premise that you are throwing money away if you rent, and making money if you buy. In reality, that is rarely true in the short run, and may be true in the long run—depending on the market. In the short run, it's difficult to recover the closing costs. You bear all the costs up front, and must wait for appreciation to recover them—which takes time. In the long run, owning your house may be profitable over renting, if the appreciation is great enough to cover those expenses as well as the interest you have been paying.

Most financial comparisons I've seen calculate five years as the average break-even point for recovering the closing costs, assuming an average appreciation. In other words, you should plan to stay in a house at least five years to recover the closing costs. This is why it is a better financial choice to rent rather than buy, on average, during residencies and the preliminary years in your first practice, since you may need to move again in less than five years.

Let's look at a hypothetical situation to compare the costs of renting versus owning a house, if you were to move to a new job after only two years. In this example, housing values appreciated, and you were able to sell your house for more than you paid. That makes this a better scenario (for the owner) rather than a worst-case scenario, for a rent versus own comparison. This example illustrates the high cost of buying and selling a house.

Assume the rental house monthly payment was equal to the monthly mortgage payment (including principal and interest, taxes, and any insurance) on the purchased house. This example assumes, for the rental house, that you were renting on a month-to-month basis and didn't have to contend with breaking a lease—which is not always the case; you will likely lose your deposit and be charged several month's rent if you break a lease. It's worth investigating lease laws in the state where you live, so you understand the costs. The purchased house appreciated 4% per year, which is about average. Suppose you paid $400,000 for your house, and two years later sold it for $432,000. You then bought a new one at that same price ($432,000). Selling the first house took ten months after the move, so you had to make an extra ten house payments. Both mortgages were at 5% interest for 30 years. The following table shows the details.

# COSTS OF RENTING VERSUS BUYING A HOUSE

| Expenses | Rented | | Owned | |
|---|---|---|---|---|
| | Monthly Payment | 2-Year Total | Monthly Payment | 2-Year Total |
| **1st House** | | | | |
| Rental deposit | $ 0 | $ 1,000 | $ 0 | $ 0 |
| Down payment (5%) | 0 | 0 | 0 | 20,000 |
| Closing costs (3%) | 0 | 0 | 0 | 12,000 |
| Monthly Payments | 2,900 | 69,600 | 2,900 | 69,600* |
| Repairs | 0 | 0 | 100 | 2,400 |
| Selling broker's fee (5%) | 0 | 0 | 0 | 21,600 |
| Selling closing costs (1%) | 0 | 0 | 0 | 4,320 |
| Add'l 10 payments (empty) | 0 | 0 | 2,900 | 29,000* |
| **2nd House** | | | | |
| Rental deposit | 0 | 1,000 | 0 | 0 |
| Down payment (5%) | 0 | 0 | 0 | 21,600 |
| Closing costs (3%) | 0 | 0 | 0 | 12,960 |
| First monthly payment | 3,060 | 3,060 | 3,060 | 3,060 |
| **Total Expenses** | | 74,660 | | 196,540 |
| **Return (1st House)** | | | | |
| Deposit | | 1,000 | 0 | 0 |
| Down payment | | 0 | 0 | 20,000 |
| Principal from payments* | | 0 | 0 | 16,640* |
| Appreciation | | 0 | 0 | 32,000 |
| **Total Return** | | 1,000 | | 68,640 |

| Net Cost (Expense - Return) | $73,660 | $127,900 |
|---|---|---|

*The 2-year total of 1st house payments includes 16,640 principal and 52,260 interest.

The overall cost, out of your pocket, was $127,900 to buy and $73,660 to rent. You would incur more than $50,000 in additional expenses to buy a house instead of renting, in this two-year move scenario. Two years was not enough time to recover the transaction costs. Even if you lost your rental deposit and had to pay additional rent to break the lease, the rental was still the less expensive option.

What would have happened if the house appreciated less than 4% per year? What if it went down in value during that particular two-year period? Housing prices can fluctuate wildly. The longer you are in the house, the closer the appreciation will get to the average and the better your odds are of profiting over renting.

In this example, even if the house sold right away and you didn't have to pay the $29,000 in extra payments, you still lost money compared to renting. Also, you would likely have rented an even less expensive house than used in this example, which would save even more money.

It's unlikely you would lose money by missing out on a short-term market jump in your area—which would have to be very large—but it is possible. You will still be OK. Houses will still be available in two to four years and they might be more expensive, but they also might be less expensive. You don't know for sure.

But you do know the closing costs and broker's fees incurred by purchasing a house will not likely be recovered in the short-term, and that by renting initially, you'll be much more flexible during the first few years. Maintaining flexibility could have some great rewards. Let's look at some other advantages and disadvantages of renting versus buying.

## Advantages of renting

You can move in with a small amount of money, usually the first month's rent and a deposit. You don't need a down payment at a time when most doctors have little money in the bank. You can get in on a few days' notice. You have no costs for repairs; in a rental, the landlord bears those costs and takes the time to make the repairs. There are no property taxes to pay. Renters insurance costs much less than homeowners insurance. You can usually leave with 30 days' notice, unless you signed a lease.

## Advantages of buying

There is a pride of ownership. You have a chance to gain some equity and build wealth. You can personalize things more since you own it, and don't need permission to paint or change things. It feels more stable, like you are here to stay. You might get a tax write-off in some circumstances (but it won't be as large as you think).

## Disadvantages of renting

The monthly payments won't build equity. You can't control changes like rent increases and how or when repairs are done. Rent is not a deductible item on your taxes. You can't paint or remodel as you wish. Depending on your landlord and the state in which you lease, breaking the lease may be costly.

## Disadvantages of buying

The higher costs of getting into and out of a house include closing costs, loan fees, inspection fees, and added escrow expenses. Getting through escrow and closing on a mortgage may take up to four months—much longer than the few days needed to get into a rental.

The paperwork burden is much greater to buy, and it takes longer to sell a house than it does to give 30 days' notice. You may be taking a big risk on market fluctuations; if you decide to leave in two years and the market is down, you may not be able to sell the house for what you paid. You may be stuck with it until the market returns, and possibly forced to be a landlord against your will. A drop in market values could put you at risk for bankruptcy. Insurance costs will be higher. Property taxes will need to be paid, in some states. You bear the costs and hassle of repairs.

## Weighing the factors

For a time frame of less than five years, the rental is likely to be the better choice for both convenience and cost. Until you've had time to get settled at the new practice, you really don't know if you made the right choice. It will be an advantage to be able to easily pick up and move.

After you have been there a few years and are convinced you like the fit, begin your search for the perfect house. You will know the area by then and will make a better selection when you are not rushed. You can choose a good neighborhood that's convenient to your work—so you won't have an unnecessarily long commute.

Time will be a precious commodity. Locate your house close to work so you can spend more time with your family and less time with your car. Other advantages of living close to your work include becoming an integral part of the community, and being close to your kids' school so you can get to events easily. My office was only a few blocks from my children's school and I could go see them play in a concert between patients, and no one knew I left. That isn't possible if you don't live close to where you work.

When the time is right, buy less house than the bank will approve. The loan officer or mortgage broker may push you to stretch your budget to the max, but don't go for it—that's not a comfortable place. Keep your mortgage under two and a half times your gross annual income. This will leave breathing room in your budget.

Weigh the advantages and disadvantages listed above, and come to the conclusion best suited to your family. You have a long life ahead, and you don't need to rush into buying a house as soon as the starting gates open. Housing is a very personal matter; it is your home, and where you will live and raise your children. You may have memories of the home where you were raised and are anxious to start some traditions with your new family. But make no mistake, you don't need to rush to purchase a house.

## UNDERSTAND THE LONG-TERM IMPLICATIONS

You are at a crossroads in your life. Many decisions made in the first two years of your practice will start you down a path that gets harder to change as time goes by. Following through with one decision—buying too much house—can illustrate the point.

If the house payment takes up too much space in your budget, another area of the budget must be reduced to make up for it. You only get to use 100% of your money. Which area will be sacrificed? Is it the children's college fund? Your retirement fund, or vacations? Will it be your cars or your savings? Or giving to your church?

Frequently, when I speak to doctors who are feeling constrained financially, the problem can be traced back to a large mortgage which has become "golden handcuffs." The longer you stay in the house, the harder it is to give it up, for both you and your family. You get used to the size, the neighborhood, and the prestige of the house. When you finally realize the cost of the house is negatively affecting your life, it is very hard to make a change. This single decision can translate into delaying your retirement. Do you want to work an extra ten years for a bigger, more expensive house? Or, would you trade every Wednesday off during your entire career for the bigger house? Wouldn't it be better to have a nice but less expensive house, and retire at 62 instead of 72? How much time will you lose with your spouse and kids by working extra for the larger house? Realize that this is the choice you are making.

Other decisions with long-term impact include the town or city where you live. If you pick a city you or your spouse don't like, you could be unhappy for the rest of your life. I remember one wife who left her husband with a note saying, "I don't want to spend the rest of my life in a town that thinks a four-wheel-drive tractor pull is a big event."

If you pick business partners you don't like, you may dread going to work each day. If your hiring institution doesn't treat doctors well, you will despise your employer every time you admit a patient.

On the other hand, when you choose your path well, life can be fantastic. You love to fish and you live on a world-renowned river for salmon fishing. You love to ski and the slopes are 35 minutes away. You love live theater and live in a city with seven theater production companies. You like the quiet life and live on 30 acres, only eleven minutes from the hospital. You grew up in an apartment in New York City and now live in the same complex as your parents, and it feels like home. You love to travel and live 30 miles from the hub airport of a major airline.

The joy or dread you experience in your job for the rest of your life could be decided by the road you take as you leave your training and start out in practice. I believe the problem of physician burnout often stems from making the wrong decisions about what you want at this juncture of your life. Choosing a job you don't like because they offered $30,000 a year more income is a path to disaster. You can make enough money to live a nice life. First, figure out what "a nice life" means to you, and then go get it.

I picked well with my first job, and practiced there for twenty years before retiring to work part-time. Interestingly, I almost worked somewhere else, and I believe things would have been very different had I taken that first offer. I'm not sure I would have worked there for twenty years.

Strive hard to start off in the right direction and you will find life to be grand. When you love to go to work every day, it is a blessing to be a doctor and your family will notice.

When **DR. ROLEX** moved to her first town, renting didn't sound very appealing so she bought a house on the country club's golf course. It was a bit of a stretch financially but she would be making good money, so it would all work out. The entire sign-on bonus came in handy for the down payment. She was accepted for membership at the country club and looked forward to her new life as an attending. She fully furnished her house with new furniture from a local store for zero down with no interest or payments for six months.

Her home was quite a long commute from the hospital, but that's what it takes to have a nice house near the city. One of her partners quit shortly after she started, increasing her workload significantly. She grew unhappy at work and when she finally decided to find a better practice, she was feeling a bit burned out.

The housing market was a little soft when she moved to the new city, and it took fourteen months to sell the old house, during which time she still had to make the house payments. She didn't have enough money to buy a new house and pay for the old house, so the second time she rented until she could get caught up financially. When her old house finally sold, it was only enough to pay off the mortgage and there was no money left after the transaction. The drop in the housing market had wiped out her equity, and her down payment was lost.

She learned the hard way about buying a tail for her malpractice insurance. That was $30,000 she had not anticipated. Because all her money was spent on the house, vacations, and fun, with nothing left over for savings, she had to borrow money from her parents to pay for the tail.

When she looked into buying life insurance, it was very expensive for the amount she wanted. She was relatively young and healthy, and felt her risk of dying was very low, so she did not buy any at first. Later when she was more stable financially, she bought some universal life insurance, but it was not enough to meet all her family's needs if she were to die. Consequently, she was underinsured and put her family at risk of financial ruin if she were to die.

Her lifestyle choices did not leave her enough financial cushion for unexpected costs. Buying a house before being sure of the practice cost her a lot of money. It took several years to recover from the expense of that job change. Her net worth did not rise much during the first few years of her practice.

After working out a new budget based on her attending salary, **DR. TIMEX** decided to rent a house at first. She wanted to use the first few years to get a good financial base and put some savings in the bank. The sign-on bonus was a good start. She knew she would be buying into the partnership in two years and wanted to be ready. She did increase her spending a little from what was budgeted in residency but only up to half her income.

She became a partner after the second year, and two years later she bought her first house. She had saved enough money for a substantial down payment. The mortgage on her house was only two times her income and fit nicely into the household budget. There was enough money left over to do all the fun things her family enjoyed, which had drawn them to this town in the first place.

Dr. Timex met with a life insurance agent early on and together they calculated how much life insurance would be needed to take care of her family if she died. She purchased a twenty-year level term insurance policy, and she feels good knowing her family will be protected in the event of her death.

She furnished the house a little at a time, as they saved up the money to pay cash for items. Slowly expanding her lifestyle and picking the right practice the first time put Dr. Timex hundreds of thousands of dollars ahead of Dr. Rolex, after only a few years in practice. The outcome of their different trajectories is already significant.

# Chapter 7

# SETTING PERSONAL LIFESTYLE GOALS

## UNDERSTAND PRIORITIES

Your family is your future. The job you take now may not be the one you have ten years from now. At some point you will retire, and not have a job at all. Your family will be there for the rest of your life. Take good care of them.

Placing your family ahead of your career is the opposite of what many doctors do. For them, work is their priority.

During your training, your family put up with your absurd work schedule, hoping life would be more normal later. It's time to dump the resident work schedule and re-engage with your family.

**Plan your life and fit work into it, instead of focusing on your work and fitting your life around it.**

## Schedule family time from the beginning

Spending time with your family doesn't just happen; you have to make it happen. If you look for leftover time to give them, you will still be looking because there is no leftover time. You must make the time and put it in your schedule.

As you move into this new era, create a livable schedule from the outset. If you cram your workweek to the gills at the start, it will only get worse as your practice grows. There are more patients out there than you can see. You can't do it all, so make sure you set some limits at the office to keep this onslaught of patients in check.

If you want to be a soccer coach for your child, then do it. Put it into your schedule so your staff knows it's protected time. Train them to respect your schedule. If you let them pile on more work, that's exactly what they will do.

Take inventory of your priorities. Write them down and review them quarterly. Being a professional in any field can easily take over your entire life, yet there are other things in your life besides work.

Ancillary work will try to creep in as well. Committees, chart reviewing, continuing education, and many other important things will all take your time. You only have 24 hours a day available and you will use 7–8 hours to sleep and 8–10 hours to work, leaving only about 6–9 hours for everything else.

You'll need some time for eating, exercising, spouse time, kid time, friend time, and even some downtime for you to recharge during the day.

If you want to see your daughter's recital, put it in the schedule and don't be late. If your spouse would like you home for dinner every night, then make it happen. No meeting is so important it should interfere with family time, unless you are the one in charge of the meeting. But if you are in charge, why didn't you move the meeting to a better time? Committees have many members, but you are the only mom or dad your child has.

You may have different priorities than I describe here. Maybe you don't want to see your child's fifth-grade band concert. Be sure the family understands it's not your thing. If they know you're not coming, they won't be disappointed when you don't show up. Be honest about it up front.

If you put your career ahead of your family, you will never see them. A doctor's job can be endless. You will always have a good excuse for them—after all, you are a busy doctor and what you do is very important.

Now is the time to set the tone for the rest of your life. Once you get the ball rolling, momentum will take over. Set up your practice like a workaholic, and that's what you'll be. But set up your practice in moderation, and you will find you can fit more into the day than you thought possible.

*You don't have to die in order to make a living.*

*- Lynn Johnston*

## Spouse time

Your spouse deserves time with you and lots of it. Not the left-overs after you are dead from a long day's work. What parts of the day do they feel are most important for you to be present? Is it getting the kids off to school in the morning? Tucking them in at night? Is it being home for a family dinner? Weekends? Vacations?

Once you know what your spouse feels is important, put it in the schedule and do your best to keep it there. My wife valued having the whole family home for dinner. She wanted me to call when I was on the way home so she could have dinner ready. If I was going to be later than usual, she wanted a call so she could plan for that. Often, I wouldn't get all my charting completed, but dinner time was upon me. I would stop and go home for our family dinner. Later, after spending some family time and putting the kids to bed, I would finish my charting. Be flexible. I had an erratic schedule and my wife did a lot to work around it.

Keep in touch throughout the day. Keep them informed if your schedule changes. Put them on the top of your priority list and you will be rewarded. Pick one night a week to go on a date with your spouse. It doesn't need to be fancy; it just needs to be time together. Even a walk in the park will do.

## Time with your kids

Not everyone will have children but if you do, they are a great responsibility. Over the last few decades as the pace of life has accelerated, there's been a movement to emphasize the "quality time" concept. Somehow it is believed that your kids will be happy with just a little time with you, if you make that small amount really count. Don't you believe it, it's a bunch of baloney. Quality time is what those who don't make enough time for their kids call it, to justify spending so little time with them. It's merely rationalization. Kids want *quantity* time.

Work fast and efficiently, and get home to the kids. Do what you can to spend time with them as much as possible. Take them to events so you can spend time talking with them in the car. Go for bike rides and walks through the neighborhood. Go to the park and feed the ducks. They just want you there. You won't have these opportunities for long. Kids grow up faster than you realize.

,inning of the week and be sure the kids and

ı your schedule. Missing something because

hard on the kids; they do get over it, but why

e to?

## Put limits on your daily schedule

The healthcare industry has a never-ending supply of people who want your time. You can literally work 24/7 if you don't set some boundaries. Most jobs have a fixed start and stop time, but not yours. You must set the start and stop time. Every day, several people will call the office and ask to be seen right away. Never did my scheduler ask if we could work in the extra patients at 6:00 a.m. The office staff had drawn a line in the sand; they didn't come in until eight thirty.

How did the line get drawn? Someone drew it. You be that someone. If you want to always be home for dinner, tell your staff you won't see patients after 5:00 p.m. You can even leave empty slots in the schedule, so you can work in those urgent patients without added fuss.

When I started coaching my son's U8 soccer team, I drew some hard scheduling lines at the office. Tuesday and Thursday afternoons from four to six were reserved for soccer practice. The kids and parents would be depending on me to be there on time. No patients were to be scheduled after 3:00 p.m. on those days. Guess what? It happened exactly that way. If you plan it, it will happen. Once or twice each season, some emergency would pop up and prevent me from being at practice. I accounted for that possibility and had a backup parent who agreed to cover for me when needed, and it all worked out.

I hosted a visiting doctor who came to our town for a conference. At one point during the day, I told him I had to get to soccer practice. He was astonished. How could I possibly work coaching soccer into my schedule? I had the same specialty as he, and he couldn't do something like that. I told him a little secret: "I'm the boss. I tell the staff when I will work, not the other way around." He worked in an academic position and couldn't control his schedule. Within a year, he left academics and joined a private practice where he could be in charge of his schedule.

If you don't make time for your family, no one will. Do you want to see the kids off to school in the morning? Schedule it. Do you want date night every Tuesday night? Schedule it. Do you want to be home for dinner every night? Make sure your staff knows your scheduling priorities. If you want to make it to the kids' after-school events, put it into your schedule. Take control of your time and put the things in your schedule that matter most to you.

Using this method, I have been able to be a soccer coach, perform the lead in a musical, be in two plays, perform in several variety shows, do magic shows for the school district, be on the church worship team, and many other fun activities. I seldom missed my kids' school or sporting events. It is possible to take charge of your schedule and control time on your terms.

It is very easy for young doctors to fall into this trap: "I'll work really hard for a few years when my kids are young, and scale back when they are old enough to know I'm around." Those few years become a few more years and before you know it, valuable family time has slipped away and can never be recovered.

## You run your practice. Don't let your practice run you.

## Take Adequate Time Off

We all need downtime to recharge. No one is an exception to this rule. Working all the time will lead to burnout for you and your family. Establish a routine from the onset that makes it clear to everyone when you are working and when you are not.

As I stated before, I recommend you have a day during the week you can leave unscheduled and protected from call obligations. Encourage your partners to each have their own protected day off. Arrange to never take call on this day of the week. This allows you to reliably make plans. One of the most difficult things about a physician's schedule is finding reliable free time.

Weekends are a very important part of your ability to recharge. Some doctors think their patients need them to be available 24/7, and therefore don't take the weekends off. Don't be one of them.

If you are not on call for the weekend, let someone else make rounds and take the calls. You go spend time with your family, or catch up around the house. When you're on weekend call, encourage your partners to let you make rounds on their patients so they can have some downtime as well. If you are a surgeon, be considerate of your partners and don't do a big case on Friday and then leave town.

If your town has no other doctors with your specialty, you will have to get creative to get some protected time off. You may be able to cross-cover with another similar specialty. As a general surgeon, I could cover for the lone ENT surgeon, urologist, and hand surgeons. I could make rounds on their patients in the hospital on my call weekend, and give them a break even though they didn't have a partner to help. The hospital can also help by bringing in a locum tenens doctor to cover for you occasionally. It's in their best interest to keep you healthy and working. This not only includes vacations, but time to be home and off call as well. When you are on call, you can't go to a concert, drink alcohol with your dinner, play a poker tournament at the nearby casino, or go to the nearby town to do some shopping. Being on call continually is stressful, and relief must be planned.

I had one resident with the "always available" mentality, and he wanted me to call him on any night if something good came in. Because of the work hour restriction, he didn't officially put himself on call every day, but unofficially he could be available for the good stuff. He didn't want to miss anything. It was very difficult to convince him this was not a good idea. I wanted him to draw some lines in the sand ahead of time to let everyone know when he was available and when he was not. He refused to do this—even got mad at the suggestion.

## Clearly define call boundaries

If you imply you are available and someone calls you, but you are busy and can't come in, it will be a mark against you. If everyone knows you are not available, then even if they try to find you, they won't be upset when they don't. Two doctors I know show how important this can be. I won't use their real names.

Dr. Alwayson was the only specialist in his field in town and seldom had any emergencies, so he took call all the time. Since he seldom was called, he simply lived his life as if he wasn't on call at all. Many times when he was called by the emergency department, he would be busy or not available. This usually made the calling doctors pretty hot under the collar. He was listed as the guy on call and he wouldn't come in. He had a bad reputation amongst his peers.

Dr. Mostlyon was also the only specialist in his field in town and had few emergencies. He listed himself on call for some days and not on call for others. When he was on call and you called him, he responded. If the emergency department called when he wasn't on call and he couldn't come in, no one was mad at him. After all, he was not on call. Sometimes, even when he was not on call, if he was free he would come in. He had a good reputation amongst his peers, even though he probably responded and declined the same number of cases as Dr. Alwayson.

Both of these doctors were sometimes not available, but one of them didn't make it clear—and it caused strife. Make it clear when you are available, and then be available. Make it clear when you are not available and go recharge your batteries. If you don't draw some lines, you will be abused.

Back in the seventies, my grandfather was the superintendent at a mill and he set no boundaries. He was always available if needed. Consequently, he would be called for every little thing, day or night. Sometimes he would get poor sleep for days in a row because of these calls. One night my grandmother took it upon herself to draw a line in the sand. She went into the other room at bedtime and took the phone off the hook so nobody could call, and he got one good night's sleep. The next day, he was asked why no one could get through to him during the night, and he told them he didn't know. When they couldn't reach him, they solved the problem without him. He really wasn't needed. He had never drawn a line in the sand and he was abused. They could solve the problems without him, but they called him because he was available. Define your boundaries and that won't happen to you.

Figure out when you are available for your family and when you are available for work. Then, both parties will understand. Your family will be just as upset if you say you will attend the game and don't make it, as your colleagues will if you let them down. If you say you will be there, be there. When they know you are committed, the occasional emergency will not upset them too much; they will understand.

## Plan vacations in both budget and schedule

Vacation is different from other time off, such as weekends. A vacation is an extended break from your usual routine. It is just as important, if not more so, than the little breaks during the week. The big difference is the loss of income that can come with a vacation if you are paid on production. Unfortunately, many doctors find themselves in a financial position where they are afraid to take time off due to its accompanied loss of income. Never let your finances get so out of control that you are not willing to take vacations. If you do, you will not be far from burnout.

Only while on vacation do you really get a chance to unplug your mind and drop the stress level. One day off doesn't adequately relieve stress from your body. You work under a high level of stress continually. You take it home, and wake at night with it. It doesn't really let up. It takes several consecutive days off for the stress to subside.

When my kids were young, we took a three week motorhome trip every summer. It usually took the entire first week for me to get unwound and forget the cases I left behind. By the second week, I was beginning to fully enjoy myself. By the third week, I was truly revived and ready to go back to work. I learned on my first long vacation that one week was not enough to relieve the stress and hit the reset button. If you take just one week vacations, your stress level may not ever fully recover.

Doctors and pastors are two groups who have the on switch stuck and never really get away from work. These are two groups who can benefit from a sabbatical, or extended time off. I have taken four of these during my career: two for four weeks, one for six weeks, and one for three months.

You don't realize how much the stress affects you until you get away for a few weeks. Consider setting up a periodic sabbatical of four to six weeks or more, every four to six years, for each of your partners. You will see the benefits after you do the first one.

# GET EXERCISE AND SLEEP

Besides taking care of your family, you need to take care of yourself. Your own health is usually the last thing on your mind. Without adequate exercise and sleep, you will become fatigued and unable to do your job well.

### Make getting enough sleep a priority

Adequate sleep is more important than you think, yet it's often the first thing sacrificed when time is short. What's adequate for different people may vary, but six broken hours is not enough. If you need a cup of coffee in the morning to get started, you probably aren't getting enough sleep. You should wake refreshed in the morning and ready to tackle the day. If that doesn't describe your mornings, start going to bed earlier each night until you wake refreshed. Then you will know the amount of sleep your body needs.

Taking call at night will be disruptive enough to your sleep schedule, without adding to the problem on non-call nights. Don't habitually stay up late doing paperwork, and then get up early to make rounds. An occasional night of poor sleep, which can't be avoided when you take call, is very different from perpetually getting poor sleep.

My wife and I took a premarital class at the end of my fourth year of medical school, and they posed the following question: "What is one thing you have learned about your future spouse in the last month?" I had recently finished my ophthalmology rotation, with no night call, and for the first time since we met, I was sleeping well every night. My future wife answered, "I noticed he is a whole lot nicer when he gets enough sleep." I never noticed this but she sure did.

## Exercise

The next item sacrificed by the time-crunched doctor is exercise. You must purposely put this in your schedule or it will not happen. You are forever suggesting your patients get more exercise, but do you do it yourself? Practice what you preach. Exercise is an important part of your well-being. It gives you more energy to get through the day. Your heart will be healthier and your muscles stronger. Stamina improves as well. You will feel a lot better when regular exercise is part of your routine. If you are feeling run down, it can often be traced to a lack of adequate exercise. Exercise gives you more energy, makes you feel better, and promotes better sleep. Exercise expert and motivational speaker Chalene Johnson puts it this way when asked how often we should exercise:

# Only exercise on days you want to improve your mood.

Lack of exercise never used to be a problem in our society. Everyone worked hard all the time. Jobs were strenuous. Now our society has lots of jobs with no exercise at all. Doctors fall into this group, sitting or standing all day long, or taking the elevator instead of the stairs. You'll often hear doctors say, "I walk all over the hospital." Walking around at the hospital is activity, not exercise. Your heart rate doesn't approach 140 and you don't break a sweat. Both resistance and aerobic training need to be part of your routine. Make the time to get a real workout at least four times a week. Do it with your family and you get some bonus time together. You will feel better and your family will feel better, and you will set a good example for them and your patients.

I know of several doctors who make lunchtime an exercise hour. They go to the gym, go for a power walk, or go jogging. Do it with your spouse and you get exercise, recharge time, and a date all rolled into one.

## ESTABLISH YOUR REPUTATION AS AN AAA DOCTOR

When I was a young surgeon, one of my senior partners pulled me aside to have a talk with me. Seems I was being a bit rough on the nurses and if I kept it up, they could make my life miserable. Over breakfast one morning, he told me about becoming an AAA doctor. To be successful I would need to be thought of as Able, Available, and Affable. My affability with the nurses needed some work. As people meet you and work with you those first few months, you will make an impression, good or bad, which will likely stick with you for the rest of your career. Make sure you are setting the tone you want, from day one.

## Able

*Having considerable skill, proficiency, or intelligence.* I guess this one speaks for itself. Everyone you encounter must feel you have sufficient skill to do your job, or you won't have a job to do. Your staff, your patients, and referring doctors must all have confidence in your abilities.

Your ability will be on display when you first begin your practice. If you are a surgeon and you have some major complications right out of the gate, it will be hard to recover. If you are a dentist and in the first month you pulled the wrong tooth, word will get out. The chiropractor who adjusted an elderly patient's neck and fractured a vertebra will not be getting many referrals for manipulation.

People will be watching you very closely with the first few patients they send you. Be darn sure you keep your nose clean as you get started. If you see a problem patient who is likely to have a complication, have your senior partner tackle that one. They already have a reputation and if the expected complication happens, it won't hurt their already-built reputation. Make sure to have a reputation for quality work before you tackle the complicated stuff.

## Available

*To be at someone's disposal, accessible, handy, convenient, present.* If it isn't easy to reach you, people will stop calling. If the referral process to get to see you is too cumbersome, they will go where it's easier. Make sure everyone knows you are available to help them if they need you.

I heard of one surgeon who would turn off his pager when he went into surgery. He felt the patient on the table deserved his full attention. When the emergency department paged him, they got no response and would have to go on a hunt to find him. They would get frustrated and eventually give up and look for someone else.

I understand what he wanted to do, but it hurt his reputation. It would have been an easy solution to give his pager to the receptionist for the OR and have her answer the pages and take a message. Then, the emergency department physician could make one call and know the doctor was in surgery and would be coming to take care of the problem as soon as he was free.

Being available doesn't mean letting patients and staff call at all hours—make expectations clear, and no one will be disappointed or frustrated. Think carefully about how to do this with your staff's and patients' welfare in mind. Now is the time to set ground rules as to how you will run your practice. Do you expect everyone to be on time and get started promptly at 8:00 a.m.? Then you be there promptly at 7:45 a.m. Do you want an undisturbed time for lunch? Make sure you adapt a schedule leaving lunch open. Do you want to have the weekend off if you are not on call? Make it clear to everyone you will be gone. Will you see your own patients in the hospital or have the hospitalist see them? Be sure people know.

Become well known for being easy to contact and happy to aid those who call. When doctors send you patients they are concerned about, call them back personally to provide follow-up. They will appreciate the feedback and be more likely to send their patients to see you in the future. You will not get a second chance to make a good first impression.

## Affable

*Friendly, good-natured, easy to talk to, cordial, warm, pleasant, likeable, nice, personable.* Who wants to have a primary care doctor who is mean or irritable? People are drawn to you if you are likable. Nurses will be more likely to let a question wait until morning rounds if they like you. Otherwise, expect to get 2:00 a.m. calls to be sure Mrs. Smith can have some Tylenol for her headache.

Hang out around the water cooler. Help your staff with their personal problems. A friendly doctor is a busy doctor. People will want your services.

## ESTABLISH YOUR OWN PATTERNS

After retiring from my long-term practice and beginning part-time work in rural hospitals, I recognized how much people get attuned to patterns. The surgeon at one hospital I covered had been there for years and always had the hospitalist consult on his diabetic patients. My style was to take care of these patients myself, if the diabetes was not out of control. One day my diabetic patient arrived on the floor after having his appendix out, and the nurse, without asking me, paged the hospitalist to let them know the patient had arrived. For years the diabetic patients always got a hospitalist consult, and that ingrained pattern was hard to change. Teach your colleagues what you want from the beginning, because by the end of your second year in practice, it will be set in stone.

You will also be inheriting your partner's patterns and reputation. For the first two years of my practice, everyone was comparing me to my partner and kept telling me, "That's not how Dr. Deatherage does it." You will start with their history and eventually establish your own, but it will take a while. Eventually I overheard someone tell Dr. Deatherage, "That's not how Dr. Fawcett does it." I knew then, I had finally established my own reputation.

## MANAGE YOUR COMMITTEE OBLIGATIONS

As you begin your career, there will be other obligations you will be asked to meet. Each of these will be for a good cause and probably come with no increase in pay. They will all take time away from your family without advancing your personal goals much. When you volunteer, it should be because what you are doing is a worthy cause to you, not merely a worthy cause to someone else. One of the big time-stealers is hospital committees. One of my mentors, whom I looked up to with great admiration, once jokingly told me, "Never turn down a committee appointment and never go to the meetings."

You should never say never, but his joke illustrated a good point. If you turn down the appointment, the powers that be will get upset. They all believe committees are vital to the smooth running of the hospital. They get paid to attend, but you don't. You are expected to attend out of the goodness of your heart, despite the fact you were on call last night and didn't get enough sleep or see your family. You can bet the administrators were home for dinner last night and slept nine hours as well.

If, on the other hand, you don't make it to the meetings, they understand because you are a busy doctor and are making them lots of money. Most hospital committees are really not worth your time. Let the chairman of the committee and the people who are paid to be there take care of business, and you attend only when it's convenient. Having one doctor on their committee is enough. They don't need you to be the fourth.

When I was younger, I went to all the committee meetings. I even chaired some committees. As I aged I began to realize they got along fine without me. If I wasn't the chair, I really wasn't needed. No more work got done because I was there, and not much got done anyway. I developed a new rule; no committee meeting outranked one of our family activities. If it didn't interfere with anything else on my schedule and I thought something productive would come of the meeting, I went. Otherwise, I had better things to do. The older I got, the fewer of my precious 24 hours got wasted in committees. They were able to run the department just fine without me.

Much more good will come of your time if you go home and have lunch with your spouse. There will be a time for you to take your turn as the chair of a committee and when you do, then do your best. I spent several years as chief of the trauma committee, two years as vice chief of surgery, and two years as chief of surgery. We each must shoulder some responsibility on committees along the way. Make sure it doesn't take too big a bite out of your life, otherwise skip it and go have fun.

When I was the chief of surgery, our hospital had 30 named committees and sections, chaired and vice-chaired by 33 physicians. There are more today. Most of those committees had more than one physician on them. That adds up to a lot of doctors giving time to the hospital for free. I believe you should be on only one committee at a time every few years to cover your perceived obligation, and preferably get paid for your time. Don't let free committee work become habit-forming. If you can, chair the committee on reducing the number of committees. Most of all, don't accept the chair position on a committee during the first five years of your practice. Wait until you have some experience to bring to the table.

## BUDGET YOUR TIME AND MONEY

When it comes to making a budget, there are two kinds of people: those who do and those who don't. There are also two kinds of budgets: one for the best utilization of your limited income, and one for the best utilization of your limited time. Both of these items, money and time, have a finite amount available for your use. If you blow some money, you can always earn some more. If you blow some time, it's not recoverable. Time is more precious than money.

## Time budget

There are only 24 hours a day, so you must use your time wisely. More people and organizations will want your time than you can ever expect to fulfill, making it important to identify your priorities before they ask for your time. Your family and your practice are two of the biggies. PTA, different boards of local organizations, church activities and committees, Rotary and other organizations, hospital committees, local and regional groups in your specialty, local charities, and others who would love to have the good doctor on their team need to come in lower on the list—or not at all. There are too many good things to do and you can't do them all. Be sure the most important ones get your attention.

In addition to scheduling time for your family, it is imperative for you to set some boundaries for your time in other areas of your life. To do this, you must first establish your priorities and goals. Once you know where you are headed, you'll know if the activity you are being asked to do will help you achieve those goals, or delay your progress.

This year I set a goal to finish this book and get it published and available to help doctors successfully establish their practices and plan the journey towards their life's goals. After setting this goal, I was asked to coordinate our church Christmas Eve service. I did this last year and it was a big success, so they wanted me to do it again this year. When I was thinking about it, my wife asked me if doing so would help me reach my goals this year. The answer became crystal clear.

I knew exactly how many hours/days/weeks of work went into last years' Christmas Eve service, and doing it again this year would slow my progress on the book. Even though it was a good thing and a thing worthy of my time, it did not fit into my plans this year. For me to accomplish what I set out to do, I would need to stay on task and turn down all the other good opportunities coming my way. You can't do everything, so you must pick the things you will do and do them well. If I do the Christmas Eve service, 200 people will benefit. If I finish the book, thousands will benefit—and I will complete a goal that's important to me this year.

## Don't let good things get in the way of great things.

Once you have established your priorities and goals, make a time budget to get them accomplished. Start with an annual timetable and work backwards. Set the vacations for the year and any other big events for the family, and work everything else around them. Birthdays, anniversaries, and holidays go in first. For my entire practicing career, I planned these events first and thus established which weekends I would be available to be on call, not the other way around.

Next is a monthly schedule. You should be able to keep this on your smartphone and have it synced with your home computer. My wife and I keep one schedule on an online calendar; thus her phone, my phone, and the computer are all in sync. If she wants to know what I'm doing today, she can see my calendar. She puts her events onto the calendar so I will know what she has planned. We can better coordinate our lives if we can see each other's schedule.

Then you have your daily schedule and the all-important to-do list. I believe the to-do list is the single most important thing you have to help keep your sanity. In college you learned you never catch up—the quarter just ends and you get a reset. In life after college you also never catch up, but the quarter never ends and there is no reset.

## The state of "caught up" doesn't exist.

The sooner you realize you will never catch up, the sooner you can relax about those things on your to-do list. There will always be a stack of journals, a stack of books, a list of movies, a garage to clean, an attic to sort, and charts to do. There is no end to what you want to do. I thought when I recently cut back to part-time that I would be able to catch up on everything. I didn't get any more caught up. The amount of things I wanted to do just increased. You will never catch up.

With that in mind, if you are forever making lists with too many things to finish, it becomes discouraging. List today only those things you absolutely must get done *today*. Then, when you finish them and the last item is checked off, you can have a sense of accomplishment and know you can now feel free to play or relax, because you ran out of things on today's list.

Do not keep this list on a piece of paper or sticky notes. You will be forever recopying the list. Keep it on your phone. Every phone has an app for this and if you don't have one, get one. They are free. Set up your task list in three categories: things to do today, things to do soon, and things you would like to get done someday. At either the end or beginning of the day, you can reevaluate the list and move things up the list as they gain priority. You don't need to recopy anything, simply change its priority and it's now on today's list. If you got sidetracked and didn't finish a project today, it's already on the list for tomorrow.

Your phone is always with you, and so is your list. When you have ten minutes of downtime, look at your list and see if you can accomplish something. Maybe one item was a phone call; you have some time, you look at the list, and make the call. You will get more done and the things you do will be those you have already determined were important to you and your family.

There should be something on your list every day that moves you one step closer to a long-term goal. If you do this, your goals will be accomplished, one step at a time. If the list is only full of busywork and errands, and nothing that moves you towards a goal, you will never get the important things done. You will never reach your goals.

Don't become a slave to your to-do list. Let it be a tool to help you budget your precious time for the things you feel are most important. Time is a terrible thing to waste, especially for doctors.

## Financial budget

When it comes to a financial budget, more information and options are available than you'll ever need. There are books on budgeting, programs for budgeting, and systems for budgeting. You can do it on your smartphone, tablet, laptop, desktop, or even paper and pencil. Pick a simple system you like, or a friend likes, and get started. I use a self-made Excel spreadsheet.

Whatever system you use, it should be simple and straightforward. A few tips are in order:

1.  Don't expect to get it right the first time. It takes a few months to dial in a budget, as you will usually forget things in the beginning. Think about the once-a-year items and get them into the monthly budget by dividing their annual cost by twelve.

2.  Don't leave any of the sections blank unless you truly never use the section. If you don't have children, childcare can be skipped. Putting nothing in the clothing section to make your budget balance, thinking you won't spend anything on clothes this year, is unrealistic.

3.  Be sure you actively choose a number for savings. Don't leave this for whatever is left over. There usually are no leftovers. Plan to put six months of living expenses in savings, accumulated within a year.

As you become accustomed to your new income, having a budget will help make your transition successful. If you do not *proactively* decide how you will spend your money to get the results you want, don't expect to get your intended results. Without a budget, you will be spending your money *reactively*, which may lead you down a path of uncontrolled spending and more debt.

## Don't leave out vacation

One special consideration for doctors: do not neglect or skimp on the vacation section. As already noted, this is very important to keep you refreshed. This is an area that people with tight budgets try to drop to make the budget look better. Saying you won't take a vacation this year is a prescription for burnout.

When my wife and I were newlyweds, we went to a time-share presentation (I wanted the free gift). I planned to turn them down, collect the gift, and be on our way. When the pitch was made, my very fiscally conservative wife said, "It sounds good to me."

I couldn't believe my ears. She never buys anything! I was counting on her to save me from the salesman. She wanted this, though, so we bought it and ended up with two weeks per year. Later, when we were talking about it, I learned more about what she was thinking. She felt the time-share financial expenditure would create a commitment to take a nice vacation every year. We were married when I was five months into my five-year residency, so a medical student/resident schedule was the only life we had experienced together. I was a workaholic and she knew it. Committing to a nice vacation to recharge our batteries is what we did, and we have never regretted the decision. Make sure you have room in your financial and your time budgets for vacations.

## Sample budget

I'm frequently asked to share a sample budget. I have been reluctant to do this, because general advice is not good when specific advice is needed—and your budget is very specific to your situation. Anything I put in writing runs the risk of each reader picking out the part that won't work for them, and then tossing the whole thing as not applicable.

With that in mind, I have included a sample budget. Don't look at it and say, "My rent is more than that, so it won't work for me." Adjust it for your rent. Use it as a tool to explain a concept. Invest heavily, pay down your debt rapidly, and live within your means.

This budget is based on the following assumptions, for a doctor's first practice in Eugene, Oregon:

✓ Housing: a 3-bed, 2-bath rental house for $1,500/month

✓ Debt:

- $250,000 in student loans at 4.5% interest
- $0 owed on car payments

✓ Sign-on bonus was used for the emergency fund (more than six months' worth of expenses, without the extra debt payments, so no additional amount is budgeted for savings until the debt is paid)

✓ Tax-advantaged investments were maximized for:

- 401(k)
- backdoor Roth IRAs (see chapter on retirement for more on this) for both doctor and spouse

✓ Married with two children

✓ Spouse did not work

✓ 10% of gross income was tithed to the church

Look it over as an example and make adjustments to meet your circumstances. Your budget must balance. Expenses cannot exceed income.

# PRESCRIPTION FOR FINANCIAL SUCCE$$
# SAMPLE BUDGET

| Annual Summary | |
| --- | --- |
| Gross income | $250,000 |
| 401(k) deduction | 18,000 |
| Taxable income | 232,000 |

| Monthly W2 Income | $19,333 |
| --- | --- |

| Monthly Expenses Category | Budgeted Amount | Percent of W2 Income |
| --- | --- | --- |
| Automatic Deductions | | |
| 1. Tithe/contributions | 2,083 | 10.8% |
| 2. Taxes | 5,593 | 28.9% |
| Remaining spendable income | $11,657 | 60.3% |
| All Other Expenses | | |
| 3. Housing (rent, utilities) | 2,300 | 11.9% |
| 4. Food | 800 | 4.1% |
| 5. Auto (gas, insurance, repairs for 2 cars) | 500 | 2.6% |
| 6. Life and disability insurance | 340 | 1.8% |
| 7. Debt repayment | 5,700 | 29.5% |
| 8. Entertainment/recreation | 500 | 2.6% |
| 9. Clothes | 200 | 1.0% |
| 10. Savings | 0 | 0.0% |
| 11. Medical/dental insurance copays | 150 | 0.8% |
| 12. Miscellaneous | 150 | 0.8% |
| 13. Investments (IRAs: $5,500 x 2) | 917 | 4.7% |
| 14. School and childcare (no daycare expenses) | 100 | 0.5% |
| Total other expenses (3-14) | $11,657 | 60.3% |

As you can see, it is possible to quickly pay off your student loans and save a substantial amount on your new high salary. This budget puts $29,000 a year into retirement, consisting of a 401(k) and two IRAs, while paying $68,400 a year on student loans and tithing $25,000.

When the student loans are paid off—in four years—the extra $68,400 a year can be paid toward a house, partnership buy-in, better vacations, toys, or your children's college fund. If the entire $68,400 a year was applied to a mortgage, it would pay off a $400,000 mortgage in seven years.

As I stated, this is an example—modify it to fit your situation. More money could be available for other purposes, depending on your priorities. You might not be one who tithes; less could go in the IRAs at first; you could stretch out the student loans another year or two; the sign-on bonus could be used for debt. You could even live in a less expensive house for the first few years. You need to work out a budget that will be right for your family. If you put loan repayment as a priority from the start, which will be covered in more detail in the next chapter, I believe you will be much happier, and have more money over the long run.

# Chapter 8

# MANAGING YOUR DEBT

## DEBT FROM THE PAST (STUDENT LOANS)

Almost all doctors will approach their first job with a mountain of debt. But don't despair—your new higher salary provides a great opportunity to eliminate your debt quickly.

If you are like most new doctors, you will have a tremendous urge to buy stuff when your new income starts rolling in. This is a very expensive urge. You will also forget, or want to forget, that you agreed to pay those loans back as soon as you were making the big bucks.

Paying back even a large student loan debt is very doable— if you prioritize paying it off quickly, and don't expand your lifestyle until you're out of debt. This approach minimizes the interest you will pay on this debt, and maximizes your ability to build wealth when it's gone.

There are programs and payment options that can help you pay this debt, or even pay it for you, with strings attached, of course. What follows is a summary of some of the available options.

## Loan forgiveness programs

The government is offering the Public Service Loan Forgiveness (PSLF) program. In this program, after you work in an approved program for ten years—and often your residency will count towards this—the remaining outstanding loans will be forgiven.

If you are considering this plan, you should already be repaying your loans on an income-based repayment plan (IBR). They must be government loans in your name. The longer your residency, the more you will benefit from this plan. The key is paying low monthly payments for as long as possible under the IBR to get the maximum loan forgiveness. Once you become an attending and your income goes up, your monthly payments go up to a non-subsidized value and you will have less to be forgiven.

If your residency consisted of five years of general surgery, one year of surgical critical care, and two years of cardiothoracic surgery, you will have only two years of payments at a higher physician's salary to make to get the payoff. After eight years of reduced payments on a resident's salary, your benefit will be very large. On the other hand, a three-year family medicine residency will require seven more years of essentially full payments, so the payoff will not be much.

Do not take a job simply for the PSLF program. If you do, when the ten years are up and you move to the job you really want, the costs of the job change and the move may wipe out any savings from the PSLF plan. Don't underestimate the costs of changing jobs. Remember my friend in Chapter One, whose job change cost him $174,800? On the other hand, the PSLF program works well if your dream job is with an approved organization. In the right circumstances, it can pay off.

This program has risks that you should understand and evaluate. Ten years is a long time to postpone your payments and accumulate interest. A lot can happen in ten years.

If at any time you decide to leave this qualified program, you lose the deal. If Congress decides to cut the PSLF program out of the budget, you lose. If you choose to work in a place you don't like just to get into this program, you lose. If your place of employment drops off the list of qualified locations, you lose. Only if everything lines up just right, do you win.

In order for this to work out optimally, you can't consolidate your loans for lower interest, and you must make the smallest monthly payment possible, for as much of the ten years as possible. This plan racks up the highest possible interest bill before the government will repay the balance. I believe this is not a risk worth taking.

When you borrowed the money, you did so with the notion you would pay it off when you were employed. The deal was: They loan you money, you get a great education so you can earn a lot more money, and then when you are earning the high salary from that education, you pay back the loans. Well, now is when you will fulfill that obligation.

Your income will jump so high compared to your salary as a resident, you shouldn't have any trouble paying off the loans—if it's a priority from the start. Go back and review the sample budget.

## Stretching out the payments

I have repeatedly seen doctors stretching these payments out for 23 years. Extending a loan for 23 years, that could have been paid off in four years, is ridiculous. You work hard for your money, so don't give it to the bank in interest payments. Postponing this debt repayment is very expensive.

If you stretch out a $250,000 student loan at 6.9% interest over 23 years without refinancing, you will pay $499,353, including the interest, over the life of the loan. This is double what you borrowed—and doesn't include the effect of taxes you must pay. To illustrate the point, let's round it to $500,000. You will be paying state and federal income taxes as well as social security, property, sales, gas, and other taxes—which will amount to about 40% of your income—on all the money used to pay off this loan. So you will need to earn about $835,000 in gross income, and pay $335,000 in taxes, to have the $500,000 you will need to pay the $250,000 interest and the $250,000 principal on your student loans.

Let that sink in a bit. You will have to earn $835,000 to pay back that $250,000 loan. If your annual income is $250,000, it will take 3.34 years to earn that. All the income from work you do for three and a third years will be needed to pay back your student loans. Do you really want to give those years of your life to the bank for your student loans?

## Paying it off rapidly

If you paid that $250,000 student loan off in four years, you would pay a total of $286,799. If you also refinanced at 4.5% interest, you would pay a total of $273,600, including interest. Compared to the 23-year plan, that's a difference of $225,753 dollars in pure interest/profit to the bank. After taking into account the 40% taxes you will pay, you will need to earn a gross income of $377,000 to pay that difference in interest accrued by spreading payments out over an extra nineteen years. That is 1.5 years of work at the same salary of $250,000.

Assuming you work 48 weeks per year and one weekend per month, then you work 264 days per year. (48 weeks x 5 days) + (12 weekends x 2 days). So 1.5 years times 264 working days per year equates to 396 days of work—or the equivalent of taking every Monday off for over eight years. That is what you are trading to make the extra interest payments, if you stretch out the payments from four to 23 years. It is not worth the trade.

When I was paying off my student loans and had just one low-interest loan left, I got hung up over paying off that loan at 3% interest. I kept thinking about investing that money for a higher return—and my wife kept thinking about not having any more debt. After several agonizing months of discussion on this point, I finally paid off the loan. (I had the money to pay it off sitting in a savings account, yet I resisted.) The relief I experienced the next month is hard to explain. I had no more student loans. It was an accomplishment that I resisted with great fortitude. The small potential profit I could have made with a higher-return investment cannot compare to the relief I experienced by paying it off.

## Refinancing

Refinancing all your loans, and consolidating them into one at a lower interest rate, is another very viable option to reduce the repayment cost. There are several companies providing this service. Do an Internet search for *medical school loan consolidation* to find a current list of banks offering this service.

If you do this, you are not eligible for the PSLF program. But, combining a refinance with a four-year payoff is the best of both worlds. Decreasing the interest rate by a third or more will save you over $13,000 on the four-year payoff.

I'm not a big fan of adjustable rate interest loans, as they are dangerous to your wealth. But if you truly will pay them off in two to four years, you can save a lot of money on the lower initial interest these loans provide. If you stretch out the payments, however, you may run into trouble. These loans tend to adjust their interest rates up, not down.

## Get out of debt before you start spending

The biggest key to successfully paying off your student loans quickly is to delay a big increase in your cost of living. This decision must be made at the start of your new job, as you establish your new budget. If you don't consider this immediately, you will start spending the money as it comes in, and it will be allocated to house payments, car payments, and vacations— and it won't be there to quickly pay off the student loans. This is a primary factor in establishing your initial budget.

You should make significant progress toward paying off your student loans before borrowing any more money, as in a home mortgage.

## If you find yourself in a hole, stop digging.

## – The Law of Holes, attributed to Will Rogers

For most doctors, the best approach will be to make a prudent budget which includes a heavy emphasis on repaying your student loans. Rent a house in the beginning, until the debt is under control and you are certain you want to stay in this first job. If you have enough money to also start contributing to your retirement plan, start as soon as you are eligible—but balance these two items carefully. Money put into a retirement fund is not available for your debt repayment, and vice versa.

It doesn't make sense to leave loan debt hanging over your head for 23 years, when it could have been eliminated in four. That's 23 years of worry and anxiety. Make eliminating your past debt a priority, and then when it's paid, begin to save for a down payment on a house.

I have lived both ways, with debt and without debt, and I can tell you, debt-free is far superior. I have yet to meet someone who regretted paying off their debts early.

It all boils down to determining a good budget for your situation. Everyone will be different. Kids, spouse, area of the country, income, choice to tithe, parents' needs, health issues, and size of student loan debt will all be different for everyone, so there is no standard formula.

I am appalled when I read investment advice given as one size fits all, when the advisor doesn't have enough information to answer the question—such as, "Should I pay off my school loans before I start my retirement investing?" As I stated above, there are too many variables involved to answer the question as it stands. Tailor the answer to your situation.

If you are drowning in debt, then paying off the debt supersedes all other choices until you are no longer drowning. Imagine a patient coming into the ED with a knife sticking out of his chest and a systolic blood pressure of 60. All efforts will be directed towards saving his life today. Your priority is not with the melanoma you noticed on his arm. When the emergency is over and he is still alive, then you can deal with the melanoma. Treat your debt with the same type of urgency and prevent yourself from drowning in debt first, then work on your retirement savings afterward.

Work out a budget that achieves your goals and fits into your life. Don't fly by the seat of your pants on this one, or you won't like where you land.

Don't let yesterday use up
too much of today.

– Will Rogers

## CURRENT DEBT (BUYING INTO A PRACTICE OR OTHER INTERESTS)

Even though the trend in medicine is to become an employee, it's not for everyone. As mentioned earlier, being a business owner has great advantages. Most physicians are becoming employees, but most chiropractors and dentists are not. When it comes time to become a partner and buy your share of the practice, there are some things to consider.

If you plan to be an employee with an organization and will always be their employee, you can skip this section and move on to the next section (Future Debt).

First of all, be sure you will be an equal partner. Before you accept the job, be sure you discuss the terms for becoming a partner. They should give you a letter of intent that spells out how the purchase of the partnership is intended to take place. It won't state the exact terms yet but will spell out the framework of how your buy-in to the partnership will happen.

The purchase of your share of the partnership may be a significant sum, and may require you to go further in debt—but not always. The buy-in is likely to happen before your student loans are paid off. This is another reason to postpone buying your house at the start of your employment.

There are several components to a buy-in agreement. I've listed and explained the major ones below.

## Accounts receivable

Your first year or two working in the practice will be as an employee with a guaranteed salary. As you begin seeing patients, the partnership will submit the bills to the insurance companies and the money they are expected to receive becomes the accounts receivable, or AR. They pay you a salary and they get to keep the money you generate. There is a delay between billing for your services and collecting the money. During the first few months, you collect a salary but no money is coming into the practice yet, from your work.

Initially the partnership will be losing money on you. As time goes by, the money in the AR begins to trickle in. Soon, you will bring in as much as your salary and the practice will break even. Later, your AR will bring in more money than they are paying you, and hopefully your partners will recover the money they lost in the first few months of your employment. They want you to pull your own weight.

When I started, it took about a year for the income I produced to equal the total amount the partners had paid me in salary and benefits. By the second year of my employment, they were making a profit and shared it with me as a bonus.

When it is time for you to become a partner, this AR account will be one of the assets you will purchase. It does not belong to you; it belongs to the current owners. It has a dollar value something less than its actual listed value. This is because what you bill is not what you collect. Some services will be discounted by the insurance company, and some may become bad debt. News flash: not everyone will pay their bill, even though you did the work and maybe even saved their life. Some patients simply have no money to pay for your services. Mrs. Smith, who is living on $1,100 a month, will never be able to pay the $40,000 total bill for her recent GI bleed. Even if she is only responsible for a portion of the bill, it is beyond her ability to pay.

The practice should have a good estimate of what percentage of the AR is collectible, and the value of the account should be discounted by that figure. For example, if the practice has an

AR of $500,000 and historically they can't collect on 12% of it, then the value of the account would be discounted by that 12%, or $60,000, making the true value of the AR $440,000. This is the amount of money the practice expects to collect over the next several months based on what the practice has billed. If you are buying in to become the fourth partner, you would be buying your share and hence would pay 25% of this or $110,000. That figure would represent your share of the money the practice will collect.

If you have been working extra hard and put more than 25% of the AR on the books, you should buy your fair share, maybe 32%. It is basically the money you expect to get paid when it comes in. Whatever production numbers you use to split the income, a greater share should be given to those who work harder, and that percentage should also be used to split the AR. I have heard new doctors express feelings that they are working harder than the older partners, and while it is possible, it's not usually the case. Be sure the AR is handled fairly, in proportion to production.

There are several options for acquiring this asset:

1.  You could buy your share of the AR, which is to simply pay the other partners $110,000. This should be paid to the partnership as an income shift from you to them over a period of time. Since they are not actually loaning you any real money—it is money expected to arrive in the future—you should not pay interest.

2. You can start a new AR account on your partnership date. The old AR account would belong to your partners, so they get the money as it comes in. The new AR account would belong to you as well as them, and you get your share, from that date forward, of all the new AR generated. This is harder to track and not a very easy solution.

3. You can vest into the AR. Since you had a hand in placing a portion of the AR into the business, you could vest into your portion. Each year you stay with the company, you own a larger portion of the AR until you own your full share. This, I feel, is the best option. No money needs to change hands if you stay for the full vesting period. You don't add to your already high debt load. This also protects the business if you decided to leave early. They invested a lot of money in getting you established. Your ownership can vest over five years at 20% each year. At the end of the first year as a partner, you would own 20% of your share or $22,500. After the second year, you would own 40% of your share, and so on. This would continue through the end of your fifth year as a partner, when you would own 100% of your share of the AR, the full $110,000. If at any time during this period you were to leave the practice, you would be paid your vested share of this asset. Of course, the AR is a fluid account—with money added and subtracted every month—so five years later its actual value will be different and you would own your full share.

## Hard assets

These are all the things your partners have purchased for the practice, in order for it to function. This would include tables, chairs, computers, computer software, phones, and all the other things you can see when you walk in the front door. Your partners reached into their pockets and paid real money to buy the hard assets, and you should purchase your share from them. You will need to arrive at a fair market value for these items, remembering they are now used and no longer worth the new purchase price.

For example, if these assets are currently worth $100,000, as the fourth partner you would be buying 25% or $25,000. It would be fair for them to charge you interest on this until you have paid them your share, but many practices don't. After determining the total value and interest rate, choose a loan length (term) that will fit into your budget easily. In some practices with lots of equipment, such as dentists, this will be a very large purchase. In other practices, like a pediatrician, this may be small.

## Office building

Your new partners will be working in some type of building. They are either renting this from another landlord or they own it themselves. If they rent, you will be paying your share of the rent. If they own, it will be to your advantage to own your share of the building instead of paying them rent.

The biggest obstacle will be establishing the value of the building. Those selling property tend to think it is worth more than those buying. Find a method you will all agree on, to set its value. You can get it appraised, use the real market value on the property tax bill, or go off a recent partner's purchase value. You should pay this over time with interest. Again, find the formula that will fit into your budget, but keep the payoff period as short as possible to minimize your interest expense. Prime rate plus 1% is a fair interest rate.

## Goodwill

This is something of historical note only. The old partner would set a value on the intangible things the business offers you. These include a referral pattern, a good reputation, an already-functioning office and staff. These do help you get started with a firm foundation, but you also bring goodwill to the practice. You are another person in the call schedule, you bring new knowledge, and you have built up a client base during your employment period.

Since both of you are bringing goodwill to the table, don't agree to pay for this in a buy-in agreement.

Down the road, you will be the partner who is selling a portion of your practice to a new junior partner. You will have something of value to sell. Be sure you treat them fairly, just like you wanted to be treated when you were the one buying in.

## FUTURE DEBT (BUYING HOUSES AND TOYS)

The single biggest factor in your future financial success is how you handle the purchase of your house. Your house is usually the largest wealth-sucker you will encounter, and not a wealth builder. If you buy a house that stretches your budget too thin, you will be miserable for years to come. The home mortgage is designed to pay an enormous amount of interest to the bank. Add to that the temptation to continually refinance for 30 years, or harvest equity to do a remodel or purchase a car or toy, and you will find yourself making a house payment for the rest of your life. Don't fall into this trap. Once you get onto the merry-go-round of always having a mortgage, thinking mortgage is good debt, and using your house as a piggy bank, it's a hard ride to get off.

As a doctor, you may feel you deserve the finer things in life. The house will need to be bigger, fancier, with more acreage, and the like. You may lose sight of what you need, and start reaching for wants that are slightly out of your budget or income range. I have witnessed doctors buying very expensive houses, sometimes way out of their budget range. Some doctors in their 60s, at a time when their house should be paid off, are refinancing $800,000 mortgages that will extend the payments into their 90s. How will they make the payments when they are no longer working?

Why is this happening? We have been convinced that our low interest, tax-deductible home mortgage is good debt. We have been convinced we should not pay off our mortgage and instead invest the money for a higher potential return. We have even been convinced a mortgage is not debt.

## A mortgage is still debt

Many times I speak to groups about becoming debt-free and someone comes up to me afterwards to proudly tell me they are debt-free. I will then ask them when they made their final house payment, only to find they still have a mortgage. They will then rephrase their answer to being "debt-free except for the mortgage." They did not consider the mortgage a debt, or at least not the same kind of debt as all the rest of their debt. This makes it a very bad kind of debt, a sneaky debt.

When you buy a house, remember the price includes interest. That increases the price you actually pay by two to five times the purchase price, depending on how many times you refinance and extend the terms.

Another trap you can fall into with a mortgage is harvesting equity. There are many forces pushing for this. The house has now gone up in value, but it's money you cannot spend. Why not refinance the mortgage and take an extra $30,000 for spending money? It will only add $160 per month to the payment.

What do you have to lose? A lot more than the $30,000 you borrowed, is what you have to lose. That money will come with interest attached to it, and a greater risk of losing your house if something goes wrong in your life. Many a doctor has had a downturn for various reasons, was unable to make the mortgage payment, and lost their house. The sooner you pay off the house, the sooner that risk is removed from your life.

Strive to pay off your house as fast as possible, in the same way you did your student loans. You only have a finite amount of time to earn money in your lifetime. The more money you give the bank in the form of interest, the less you will have to spend on your lifestyle and save for your future.

In order to maintain stability in your budget, never consider an adjustable rate mortgage. It is not worth the risk of losing your house when the rates go up and your income goes down.

If you will be buying into a practice, be sure you do it before you buy your house. In Proverbs 24:27, King Solomon stated, "Get your fields ready, after that build your house." What great advice. Be sure your source of income is established before committing to spending money on your house. If you do it the other way around, you could find yourself with too much house and not enough money left to buy the practice. If you buy the practice first, you know exactly what is left to purchase a house.

## Unnecessary debt

There are lots of toys out there to tempt you: cars, boats, motorcycles, vacation homes, motorhomes, airplanes, and many more. These can be a great source of pleasure for your family, but not if the payments are also sucking the life from you. I'm all for toys. I love toys and have been through my share. Don't fall into the trap of financing your toys because you need them right now. Save the money first and then pay cash for your toys. If you do so, you can pay less than the sticker price. Paying more than the sticker price in the form of interest will reduce your available wealth. The toy you can afford is the one you can write a check for.

Don't finance anything on a credit card. They are so convenient and so deadly to your wealth. They carry one of the highest rates of interest you can pay. Use your credit cards to your advantage, not your disadvantage. Get rewards, airline miles, cash back, and anything else they will offer to entice you to use their card, but NEVER let them charge you interest. A few months of interest will wipe out all the benefits.

You work too hard for your money to give it to the bank. Buying one toy on a payment plan doesn't seem like a big deal, and it probably isn't. The problem develops when payment plans become a habit, and soon you have several items purchased that are charging you interest. Then you will wake up one day and realize you are going to work every day just to make payments on your stuff. Not a happy feeling. How many days will you work this year to pay the interest on the stuff you bought last year? Or the year before?

---

**DR. ROLEX** was not too concerned with her student loan debt, or any debt, for that matter. As long as she was able to make the monthly payments, she was good. She intended to stretch out those loans over the longest period allowed, in order to keep the highest cash flow possible for her current needs. It took Dr. Rolex fifteen years to pay off her student loans.

Since she is an employed physician, she spent no money buying a practice. Consequently, she has no equity in her practice contributing to her net worth or her retirement.

When she bought her second house after moving and changing practices, she borrowed the maximum

---

amount the bank would loan on her income. Every five years or so, she has refinanced the house and harvested equity. It is usually a low-interest loan, so she considers it a good move financially. That equity came in handy to take her family on some great vacations, do some fixing up around the house, and buy a ski boat. She owes more money on her house now than she originally borrowed, and still has thirty years of payments left to make. Since she intends to keep periodically refinancing, she will have a very large mortgage when she reaches retirement. She has plenty of money coming in to make the payments, so she's not too concerned.

Over the years she has financed many things: vacations, cars, motorhomes, boats, snow mobiles, motorcycles, and a lot more. Each time, she paid the sticker price plus a lot of interest. Her family did have a lot of fun using the toys, and she has no regrets.

**DR. TIMEX** never felt comfortable with student loan debt hanging over her head. During the first few years of her practice, she kept her expenses down and made large payments on her student loans. She paid them all off in four years. She felt a great burden was lifted from her shoulders. She paid much less in interest because she made accelerated payments.

When she made partner, she acquired another set of payments to make. She worked to pay off the partnership in only five years, and again limited the interest she had to pay. She now has a substantial equity position in a medical office building, and it's appreciating in value as well as producing passive rental income. She hopes to sell the building and the practice when she retires, to supplement her retirement income.

A few years after making partner and when she was certain she was staying in that location, she bought her first house. Paying a little over twice her annual salary for the house, it was a very comfortable payment. She paid off the house in eight years and did not harvest any equity.

She never purchased any toys with borrowed money, and consequently bought things at a cash discount.

We are beginning to see a divergence between Dr. Rolex and Dr. Timex. Due to all the expensive living and extra interest Dr. Rolex has paid over the years, she has little savings apart from her company retirement plan. After many years of avoiding interest and living well within her means, Dr. Timex now has no debt and a net worth that's $3 million more than Dr. Rolex, with the same salary.

# Chapter 9

# PLANNING FOR THE FUTURE AND RETIREMENT

## ADVISORS

You will likely need to find three types of advisors, early in your career. These are a good accountant, attorney, and possibly a financial planner.

### Accountant

Ask the other doctors in town for recommendations. When I first moved to town, I asked around and two names kept coming up, so I picked one and have worked with him ever since. You are not looking for a tax preparer, which is what many people who call themselves accountants really are. You need one who can help you with planning decisions, office accounting, business deals, and taxes. They can often save you a lot of money, especially as your investing starts to get more complicated.

When I first started earning money as a resident, I did my own taxes. I thought I could fill out the forms as well as anyone else. Then I made an investment in a low-income housing real estate investment trust (REIT—similar to a mutual fund for buying income-producing property), which complicated my taxes. I had additional forms to fill out. The K-1 form that came every year also had instructions for filling out the seven new forms I needed. I did it myself. Someone told me I would save money by having an accountant do this. I didn't believe them, so I put it to the test.

The next year I did my taxes myself and then turned everything in to an accountant to see what the difference was. The tax bill was $700 less by the accountant's figures than by mine. That savings was more than his fee, and a lot of money on a resident's salary back then. That taught me a lesson. Tax laws are quite complex and they change every year, so you are unlikely to be able to keep up with them. That is your accountant's job, so find a good one.

## Attorney

As mentioned earlier, you should have your employment contract reviewed by an attorney who represents you. Establishing a relationship with an attorney has come in handy many times during my career. I have set up several LLCs and partnerships, which required an attorney's help. Starting a surgery center required an attorney. Every now and then a question comes up that I need to run by an attorney. If your attorney is familiar with you, it can be as easy as a quick phone call for advice. You will also need a will and possibly a trust.

Remember that attorneys specialize in different areas just like doctors do. If you have a good attorney and he can't help you with a new issue, he can refer you to the right attorney. That happened when I negotiated the contract to write this book. My attorney did not handle intellectual property issues, but he referred me to one who did and had a good reputation. Without his referral, it would have been difficult to find the right attorney, as there were none with the right expertise in my town.

## Financial planner

You may require assistance with some aspects of investing—how to set up retirement accounts, IRAs, and other options. In the beginning, you may need some help. Investing is not hard to do, and you should be able to handle it yourself after a little training. I used financial planners in the beginning, and after a few years was able to handle it myself. But every now and then something comes up, and I go back for advice. Evaluate your comfort level with investing, and hire a financial planner if you want or need guidance. It is best to find one who charges by the hour, and not by the transaction or a percentage of your assets.

You don't want his recommendations to be influenced because he would make more money if you do what he suggests.

I recently read the blog entry from a doctor who got bad advice from his financial planner. The planner told him to go ahead and finance an expensive car and invest his cash. His advisor got paid 1% of the value of his total portfolio. If this doctor used his cash to buy the car, it would lower the amount of fees the advisor would collect. He got advice that was best for the advisor, not the advice that was best for the doctor.

## RETIREMENT PLANNING

This is really not a book about investing, but a few tips to get you started in the right direction are in order. Whether you join a group or become an employee, some sort of retirement plan will already be set up. Plan to contribute whatever they state is the maximum amount. Only overwhelming debt that must be eliminated first should keep you from this plan. You want to have interest compounding in your favor as soon as possible. Compound interest is a big factor in your future wealth.

With your newfound income, you should be able to save even more than your company's retirement plan maximum. I would recommend you also start an IRA (a Roth if you qualify), and max it out for both yourself and your spouse.

If you don't qualify for a Roth IRA—and many doctors will not, due to their high income—you can do a backdoor Roth IRA contribution. To do this, you make a non-deductible contribution to an empty traditional IRA account and then convert it to a Roth IRA account. There will be no taxes to pay on the conversion, and the growth will be forever tax free. Even though you don't qualify to make a contribution to a Roth IRA, your traditional IRA can be converted to a Roth IRA at any time. These three accounts, the company plan and your and your spouse's IRA accounts—invested in whatever moderately aggressive option they offer—will grow into quite a nest egg by the time you are ready to retire.

I started maxing out my retirement plan, my IRA, and my wife's IRA during the first year of my residency, when we only earned a $45,000 combined annual income. Money I was able to deposit during my residency, when an IRA deposit was capped at $2,000, grew to $225,000 over the next twenty years. If I leave it alone for another twenty years and it grows at an average of 7.5%, it will exceed $1 million. That's what starting early can do for you. If I had waited to start until after my residency—a five year delay—I would have $1 million less at age 70.

As I write this, the maximum IRA contribution is $5,500 ($6,500 if over age 50). If both you and your spouse invest $5,500 annually from age 30 to age 65, you would invest $11,000 a year, or $916.67 a month, for 35 years. That would total $385,000 invested. Over those 35 years, you should get an average return of about eight to ten percent interest. Using the more conservative eight percent return, you would have $2,102,733 at age 65. The office retirement plan, which usually will have a higher contribution limit than the IRA, should have even more than that. You should have a combined nest egg exceeding $4 million by age 65 if you follow this advice.

Just get started and put this into your budget before you start spending all your money. If you are not sure how to set up the IRAs, call a brokerage firm like Schwab or Fidelity and they will help you. Don't open your IRA at a bank; they generally don't have enough investment options. If you are not sure how to invest the money, just pick a broad index fund and get started. There are several funds that fit into this category and they have the word "index" in their title, such as the Schwab 1000 Index Fund. They have a low expense ratio, and will track with their indexed section of the stock market as it moves. This will be a safe and conservative place to start, until you learn more about investing.

When I first started investing, I thought I was smart enough to beat the market. I spent several hours a month reading investment newsletters and working on finding that great investment that would help me beat the market. After a few years, I noticed that the money I managed was not doing as well as the money I parked in the index funds. It dawned on me that I had been wasting a lot of time trying to play the market. My biggest losses fell into this category. I wish I could have that time and money back. I learned the lesson and I don't even watch the market much anymore. I have other things to spend my time on. I just put the money in a good mutual fund and let it grow with the market. Don't make the same mistake I did and think you are better than the professionals, because they can't beat the market either.

I have seen too many doctors who get caught up in spending their new income and think they will begin investing later, only to never quite get around to it. They say they don't have the money to put into the retirement account, but they did have the money to buy a $60,000 car, or a very expensive house. Don't find yourself in this position. A doctor friend of mine who augmented his lifestyle to a very high position once told me, "Some of the best advice I got was from a neurosurgeon. He told me to open a Schwab account and begin contributing to the Schwab 1000 Index Fund. I wish I could still afford to do this." His lifestyle became so expensive that he had nothing left to invest. Start early, save big, and this one thing will secure your retirement.

## The richest doctor is not always the one with the biggest house and the nicest car.

# YOUR CHILDREN'S HIGHER EDUCATION

Education is getting outrageously expensive, but you know this firsthand. Your education was a good investment and has likely placed you in the top five percent of wage earners in the country. As such, your children will not be qualifying for any financial aid, other than loans or some type of athletic or merit scholarship. You and your child will be expected to bear the full cost of your child's education.

When my first child was preparing for college, I filled out the parent's portion of the Free Application for Federal Student Aid (FAFSA). I was told everyone should fill it out as you never know what you might qualify to receive. It's an online estimator of what you would be required to pay for an education. I was hoping for some aid.

After I filled out the form and submitted my financial information, I swear the computer was laughing at me. I was a multi-millionaire and earning an income in the top five percent of the country. There would be no financial aid beyond loans for my children. If you play your cards right, it will be the same for you, so plan ahead.

You will make plenty of money to pay for their schooling without any hardship on your part—if you plan it right. Many doctors don't realize this soon enough, and when their kids are applying for college, they aren't financially prepared.

I know of a two-doctor family with a combined income of over $500,000 a year, yet they make their children borrow for their education rather than help them. They have it easily within their grasp to graduate their children debt-free. What a blessing that would be.

Some of you may agree with their philosophy, that kids should stand on their own two feet. I believe this also. But I think giving them an education to start off their life is a great gift you can easily provide. It is a tremendous benefit for them, and of little consequence to your finances. Think about your own situation. How would your start have been different if you finished your training without any debt?

In the book *The Millionaire Next Door* by Thomas J. Stanley and William Danko (Taylor Trade Publishing), one I highly recommend, the authors state that paying for college was the one area of economic outpatient care you could give that was beneficial to your kids. Give them a great, debt-free start on life, the easy way. Open a 529 college savings plan and start putting away a small amount of money each month for their future education. They will get a great debt-free education and you won't notice the missing money.

Begin saving as soon as your income increases with your first job, before you advance your lifestyle. Then you will never miss the money. If, instead, you start using all your money for your lifestyle, there won't be anything left over to save for their college education.

Handle your money just like your time—there is never anything left over, so fund the priorities first.

If you were to start saving $200 a month in a 529 account at the birth of each child, what would happen? You would save for 22 years, through their college graduation. If you average a 6% return, you would have accumulated $109,000. If you average an 8% return, it would total $143,000.

My children attended the University of Oregon. The university website lists the total cost of attendance for the 2015–2016 year at $25,167, for Oregon residents. That translates to $100,668 for their entire education. My kids each did it for less than that. Even at the lower 6% return, $200 a month per child, contributed to a 529 account for 22 years covered all their costs.

Some schools cost more than this example, and many cost less. Wherever your children choose to go, an extra $100,000 in the bank will be a great help. I'm sure you could put away more than that if it was a priority, especially when all your debts are gone. If it is not a priority, you won't save anything. Which path will you choose?

**DR. ROLEX** isn't big on planning, budgeting, or goal-setting, and lives mostly for today. Her philosophy is focused on the present. The past is gone and the future is not here yet, so she doesn't worry about them. When she left her first job, she took out her retirement money and paid the penalty. She needed the money for the expensive transition and since she was young, she figured she had plenty of time to make it up. She waited until her first house sold before starting to put money into the retirement plan at the second job. Even then, she did not max out the contributions. She now has much less saved for her retirement than she could have.

With her high income, she thought she could pay for her kids' college education without needing to save. When it came time for them to apply to college, that same high income made them ineligible for any aid except borrowing. Dr. Rolex's expensive lifestyle did not leave enough to pay for college expenses, so her kids accumulated significant student loan debt, just like Mom did.

**DR. TIMEX** carefully laid out goals, and her budget included plans for rapidly paying off debt and saving for the future. She began maximizing her retirement plan as soon as she was eligible. She also put money into her and her husband's IRAs. After paying off her debt, she was even able to save more money outside her retirement plan. At the birth of each child, she started putting away $200 a month into a college fund. There was enough money in each account for her children to attend their state university and finish debt-free. She felt very proud to give her children the debt-free start on life she never had.

# Chapter 10

# PARTING THOUGHTS

Many years of living lavishly and paying interest on many items have taken their toll on **DR. ROLEX**, financially. At age 60, she has a net worth of $1.5 million, a good portion of which is home equity. She has no equity in a practice to sell. She is concerned about being able to afford to retire. She still has a substantial home mortgage payment and is not sure she can make it, if she had to live on her retirement savings. She would like to retire now, but will need to keep working for several more years before she can afford to do so.

The Dr. Rolex philosophy can be summed up in one quote:

> Wealth is not his that has it,
> but his that enjoys it.
>
> – Benjamin Franklin

> Many years of living within her income, avoiding interest payments, and maximizing her retirement plan have been good for **DR. TIMEX**, financially. At age 60, she has a net worth of $7 million. She has decided to retire and travel with her husband, now that her children are out on their own.

The Dr. Timex philosophy can be summed up in one quote:

Spend less than you earn
and do it for a long time.

– Ron Blue

The way you start and the trajectory you choose make all the difference in the world. Both Dr. Rolex and Dr. Timex lived the life they desired and were, for the most part, satisfied along the way. Since they travelled on different financial trajectories, they ended up in different places by the time they reached age 60, even though they earned about the same income. Dr. Timex was debt-free and had a $5.5 million greater net worth, and retired several years earlier than Dr. Rolex. Dr. Rolex enjoyed her toys and lavish vacations, and recovered from her job change with a little help. She found a job that fit her better the second time, and even though she couldn't retire as early as Dr. Timex, she has had a comfortable life.

Which will you be: Dr. Rolex, Dr. Timex, or a little of both? Too much Dr. Rolex philosophy and you end up spending all your money and borrowing even more. You will get to the finish line with less and still have debt to pay, but you had fun along the way. Too much Dr. Timex in the mix and you become Ebenezer Scrooge, not spending anything on today's happiness and fun while saving everything for the future.

I believe you should have a little of both. Find a good balance between eliminating your debt, living your life for today, and preparing for the future.

## THE RIGHT START

Starting your practice right requires making some early key decisions that create ripples throughout your life. Picking the wrong job and going through another job search and move can be very taxing on you and your family. Taking the steps outlined in this book will help lessen the chance of that happening, but won't eliminate it.

There are so many things to get right, like choosing the right town, the right partners, the right practice environment, and getting through your contract negotiations. There are so many opportunities for error; it's no wonder many doctors don't stay with their first job.

Getting the right start financially will allow for some breathing room in the event things don't go as planned. Getting rid of your student debt quickly and removing that burden is a key factor. Holding off on the purchase of a house and getting an early start on retirement savings are others. How you handle your finances when you get that sudden influx of money will set the tone for the rest of your life. Setting your goals and getting your budget right from the start will keep you pointed in the right direction—as long as you continue to follow your plan.

No one can make the right decisions 100% of the time. I sure didn't. But if you consider carefully, and follow the advice presented in this book, you won't be too far off target from your goals when you reach the end of your career. As you begin your journey, I would like to make one special plea to help you reach a point of maximum flexibility: become debt-free as soon as possible and stay that way.

## JOIN THE DOCTORS WITHOUT DEBT MOVEMENT

It's never too late to decide to get out of debt—but you have to want it. Debt is just one more factor weighing doctors down. Debt enslaves you to the lender, and decreases your future wealth and negotiating power. It's also a factor you can fully control. Taking back financial control could be the biggest wave of improvement in medicine since vaccines. There are many pluses to becoming a debt-free doctor.

## Handling your money well decreases stress—big time

Debt is a big stressor. Sometimes when you don't feel well, it's not clear how bad you feel until you are back to normal and can appreciate the difference. Becoming debt-free is similar. There were two points in my life when I noticed this phenomenon. The first was when I made my last student loan payment and the second was when I made my last mortgage payment. In both cases, I felt a great weight lifted off my shoulders that I didn't realize was there. Couldn't you use one less stressor?

## Reducing debt and being debt-free gives you a valuable asset . . . time

It's hard to imagine how much debt cuts into your free time. As it turns out, you feel a need to work more to pay off the debt. Many doctors don't go on vacation with their family, and instead stay home to work so they can pay the bills. You can feel free to take a day off during the week, or even an afternoon to go to a child's soccer game in a nearby city, when you don't feel the need to produce. The ability to take more time off, if you need it, will go a long way toward fending off burnout. Lower monthly expenses means a lower need to produce income, means feeling freer to take time off with less guilt and worry . . . you get the picture.

### Return the money for others to use

When you pay back student loans, that money becomes available for the next student to borrow. As tuition continues to rise, this may become a limiting factor. Now that you are earning a great living, pay the money back and let someone else use it. You don't need it anymore. They will be grateful for the opportunity and society as a whole will benefit.

### Paying off debt gives you more disposable income

After paying off your debts, interest won't be charged against you. If you don't have to pay interest, that money will be available to you for some other use. If you are carrying $500,000 in debt with an average of 5% interest, that's over $2,000 a month in interest. Eliminating that debt gives you back the $2,000 a month to spend on other needs, plus the money you were paying in principal.

The bank doesn't deserve the money more than you do. Don't give away next year's income before you even have a chance to earn it. This increase in available money could be used for a better lifestyle, more investing for retirement, college money for the kids, better vacations, and the list goes on. What would you do with the extra $2,000 a month?

## Retire earlier than you might otherwise

You may love your job and want to work forever, but why not do it because you want to, and not because you have to? Getting out of debt gives you more savings and fewer expenses. An $800,000 mortgage requires an extra $2 million in savings to pay for it in retirement. Paying off the mortgage would mean retiring $2 million sooner. Then, if you want to continue to work, it will be on your terms. You never know how long your health will last.

## Make a difference

When you are debt-free and have accumulated enough money so you don't need to work anymore, many other options can open up for you. Now that you don't need to make a living, you can make a difference. What would you do if money was not a limiting factor? What kind of difference could you make in the lives of others?

How could the country be improved if droves of doctors were in such a position? Would you like to be in a position to substantially help your favorite charity? Maybe you can work in a third world country. You can help out at a critical access hospital in rural America, or work for the local homeless shelter, taking care of people who desperately need your help. The possibilities are endless.

## Gain negotiating power

The local hospital knows you need your income, so they have all the power in a negotiation. If a group of hospitalists want the hospital to make a change but they are afraid of losing their jobs, they can be easily pushed around. If, on the other hand, all of the doctors were debt-free and no longer feared losing their jobs, they are in a position to say no to the hospital's demands. What a feeling, to be able to tell the hospital how it will be instead of the other way around.

If all doctors were in a position to walk away from a negotiation, they have power. The hospital is much more inclined to consider your way of thinking if you have some power at the negotiating table. Being debt-free gives you the confidence to stand up for your rights. If all of the doctors in America did this, what changes could we make in the healthcare system?

## Be free and help others catch the vision

Solomon stated in Proverbs 22:7 that:

## Just as the rich rule over the poor, so the borrower is servant to the lender.

Did you really go to school all those years to become someone else's servant? Another minion working for the bank? If you don't think you are a servant to the bank, try skipping a few mortgage payments and see what happens. Debt removes a piece of your freedom. Once you escape from under the bondage of debt, many new opportunities will appear. You will benefit. Your family will benefit. The patients will benefit. America will benefit. Doctors without debt will be the ultimate win-win deal. Join me in this movement.

## PRESCRIPTION FOR SUCCESS

As a young doctor, I was lucky to have financial guidance from my family and medical practice mentoring from my partners, who truly took me under their wings and taught me how to run a practice, both from a medical and a business perspective.

Medical schools do not provide career guidance or money management courses. Add to that the changing practice models from owner to employee, the costs and complexity of malpractice insurance, licenses and privileges, and the heavy debt from education, and you may feel you've just jumped into shark-infested waters.

Too many doctors are dealing with an out-of-control work or call schedule, overwhelming debt, or working in a practice or with partners they don't like. The prevalence of burnout and suicide among physicians is a clear warning that doctors need guidance to navigate these waters.

Use the information in this book to your benefit, to build the practice and the life you want to have. Even if your first job doesn't work out as you hoped and you have to move to a new one, you'll sail through it much more smoothly if you know how to steer—and if you know what to steer towards. I wish you the best for your future and your career.

# QUESTIONS? COMMENTS?

*Dr. Cory S. Fawcett*
*DrCorySFawcett.com*

I want to hear from you. Any feedback is welcome, and I want to know if you think I've missed an important topic, or you have a story to tell or found a mistake. Also, I didn't put everything I know into this book. Send me an email at DrCorySFawcett@gmail.com or contact me through my website at DrCorySFawcett.com.

If you found this book to be useful, please post a comment on my website. I'd truly appreciate it if you spread the word through social media or by posting a review on Amazon. Please pass on what you've learned to your colleagues.

**Connect** with Dr. Cory S Fawcett on LinkedIn

**Like** Dr. Cory S Fawcett on Facebook

**Follow** @drcorysfawcett on Twitter

**Email** DrCorySFawcett@gmail.com

# Acknowledgments

Many people contributed to the knowledge and experience contained in this book. My parents, Jim and Wayna Fawcett, and grandmothers, Luella Fawcett and Virginia Brown-Petko, taught me valuable lessons about living within my means and saving for the future. My uncle, Jereal Brown, gave me early financial advice and recommended books that taught me what it takes to be financially successful. I was fortunate to have this knowledge before I began to earn a living. As a result of their guidance, I started off on the right track and began saving for retirement during my internship. I wrote this book to share this knowledge about what it takes to start out right. I want to give residents starting their practices after me the same chance.

A special thanks to my wife, Carolyn, for dialing back my tendency to spend money. Fortunately, she was there when I first began to earn a living, and was a major contributor to my early decisions. Because of her, we saved more, gave away more, and tithed more than I ever dreamed possible.

I would also like to thank my first partners in practice, Dr. David Oehling and Dr. Mark Deatherage. These two took me under their wings as a new surgeon, fresh out of residency, and became my mentors. I was one of the lucky ones; I landed good partners the first time. They taught me how to run a medical office, how to keep my nose clean, how to be an AAA doctor, and many other things necessary for my success.

A special thanks to those who did the test reading of this book: Sean Traynor, MD, FACS; Larry Buglino III, DO; Vanessa Papalazaros, MD; Tyler Mittelstaedt, MD/MPH; Emily Groves, MD; Nathan Kemalyan, MD, FACS; and my wife, Carolyn Fawcett.

There are many others along the way who contributed to the information I learned and am now passing on to the next generation. I'm sorry I can't list them all, or even remember them all, as they are too numerous to count.

Thanks to the team at Aloha Publishing, including Maryanna Young and Jennifer Regner, and the Fusion Creative Works design team of Shiloh Schroeder, Rachel Langaker, and Jessi Carpenter. Without them, this book would still be just an idea floating around in my mind.

# About the Author

Dr. Cory S. Fawcett's passion for teaching personal finance spans his entire career. Through one-on-one counseling, as a Crown Financial Ministries small group discussion leader (a ten-week Bible study on money management), and as a keynote speaker, he has been improving people's financial and professional lives for years. As an instructor for medical students and residents, he has found they have a hunger and need for financial wisdom and direction, as they transform into practicing physicians.

With his financial interest and background knowledge, he has served on several boards and financial committees throughout the years. He has been involved as owner, founder, or partner in more than two dozen business and real estate ventures.

The lack of surgeons in rural areas and his desire to work less led him to the decision to retire from his twenty-year practice, in a town with ten general surgeons, and assist in underserved areas. In February 2014 he began working part-time in rural Oregon towns with only one or two surgeons. With just one surgeon in town, the call burden of 24/7 availability is unsustainable. Dr. Fawcett provides them with a needed break from their pager, helping to keep rural surgeons healthy.

His current mission is teaching doctors how to have healthy, happy, and debt-free lives—to regain control of their practice, their time, and their finances. He is writing, speaking, and coaching to improve the lives of his colleagues. Burnout, suicide, debt, and bankruptcy are increasing among physicians, dentists, optometrists, chiropractors, pharmacists, nurse practitioners, and others in the healthcare industry, and he focuses on halting the progression of these unnecessary outcomes.

Dr. Fawcett is an author, speaker, entrepreneur, and now semi-retired general surgeon. He completed his bachelor's degree in biology at Stanford University, his doctor of medicine at Oregon Health Sciences University, and his general surgery residency at Kern Medical Center. After completing his training, he returned to southern Oregon to practice for twenty years in a single specialty, private practice group in Grants Pass. Since 1988 he has shared his home with his lovely bride Carolyn. They have two boys: Brian, who graduated from college with a degree in economics, and Keith, who is currently working on a degree in mobile development.

Made in the USA
San Bernardino, CA
19 July 2020